BREEDING THE ORCHID DOTTYBACK,

Pseudochromis fridmani

An Aquarist's Journal

Martin A. Moe, Jr.

D1603737

Green Turtle Publications
P.O. Box 17925
Plantation, Florida 33318

Copyright © 1997 by Martin A. Moe, Jr.

Green Turtle Publications
P.O. Box 17925
Plantation, FL 33318

Library of Congress Cataloging-in-Publication Data

Moe, Martin A.
   Breeding the orchid dottyback, *Pseudochromis fridmani*: an
   aquarist's journal / Martin A. Moe, Jr.
      p.   cm.
   Includes bibliographical references (p.   ) and index.
   ISBN 0-939960-09-5 (pbk.)
      1. Orchid dottyback--Breeding.   I. Title.
SF458.073M64   1997
639.3'772--DC21   97-28339
                                                            CIP

Printed in the United States of America
10 9 8 7 6 5 4 3 2 1

V8 is a registered trademark of Campbell Soup Company, used with permission.

Cover Photo: The male orchid dottyback pauses in front of the rocky hole where he has made his den.
Rear Photo: Hundreds of tank raised orchid dottybacks frolic in a 50 gallon aquarium.

Dedication

To Bill and Arline Addison,

With thanks for keeping the dream alive.

Acknowledgments

Fortunately, I've made a lot of friends over the years that were in a position to help me during this project with advice, fish, supplies, and equipment. Often the help was substantial and I greatly appreciate every little bit of support and assistance. I would like to thank the following people and companies for their many and varied contributions:

Bill Addison, C-Quest, Inc.; Aquatic Eco-Systems, Inc.; Stan Brown, The Breeder's Registry; Joe and Sally Bauer; Tom Capo, Aplysia Resource Facility; Merrill Choen, Aquarium Products, Inc.; Lou Dell, American Marine, Inc.; Omer Dersom and Michael Lasky, Coralife/Energy Savers Unlimited, Inc.; Ken Di-Roberto, Marilyn's Fishy Business; Pete Escobal and Tom Aurand, Filtronics; Tom Frakes, Dennis Crews and Ed Mowka, Jr, Aquarium Systems, Inc.; David Gauss, D&D Marine Enterprises; Beth Haydon; Roy and Teresa Herndon, Sea Critters; Frank Hoff, Florida Aqua Farms, Inc.; Tim Hovanec, Bud Synder, Alice Parham, and June Heister, Marineland/ Aquaria, Inc.; Ken Hyatt, O'Dell Industries, Inc.; David Kawahigashi, San Francisco Bay Brand; Jack Kent, Kent Marine, Inc.; Joe Lichtenbert, Reef Propagations, Inc.; Ray Lucas, Aquarian Foods; Joel Martin and Gary Jones, Aquarium Pharmaceuticals, Inc.; Dr. Robert Rofen, Kordon/Novalek, Inc.; Jim Rogers and Leo Morin, Sea Chem Laboratories, Inc.; Greg Rys, Typically Reef; Ed Schnider, O.I.Sea, Inc.; David and Cathy Smith, Reef Encrustaceans; Julian Sprung and Daniel Ramirez, Two Little Fishies; Jeff Tellock; Chris Turk, Ocean Nutrition; and Steve Zimmer, Emperor Aquatics.

Of course, I can't thank everyone who gave me the gift of encouragement and appreciation, but this was always immensely helpful. Marine Aquarium Societies, right in my own back yard and over 3000 miles away were always helpful and my thanks go to them as well. Barbara, my wife and publisher, editor, confidant, critic, life partner, love of my life, fire of my loins, and many other things, deserves a very special thanks. Someday she may get that bathroom back. And thanks to our next door neighbors, Brian, Robin and Kelly, and my daughter Andrea, who feed the fish when we are away, which allows us to wander off for a day or two now and then.

Contents

Other books by Martin A. Moe, Jr.

The Marine Aquarium Handbook:
Beginner to Breeder

The Marine Aquarium Reference:
Systems and Invertebrates

Lobsters: Florida •Bahamas •the Caribbean

In preparation

Captive Propagation of Marine Tropical Fish:
A Hobbyist's Guide

The Aquarium Data Book:
Fundamental Facts and Figures

Introduction

What does it take to breed coral reef fishes? Witchcraft, magic, and a thumb as blue as the open sea, or a million dollars and a high tech hatchery? Actually, none of these are necessary, although the blue thumb will certainly be helpful. With many species, you can do it at home with a little knowledge, determination, and persistence.

I think it is very important for more hobbyists to begin to breed various species of tropical marine fish and invertebrates. The marine hobby is expanding, prices for tropical marine life are on the rise, marine life support technology is getting better and better—and negative pressures on the natural environment and the hobby are increasing. A core of successful hobbyists, breeding a variety of marine fish and crustaceans, will also do much to stimulate the growth and stability of the hobby. Only propagation efforts by many hobbyists, with various fish and invertebrates, will greatly increase the number of species under culture and considerably expand the horizons of our hobby.

The few commercial marine hatcheries in existence today cannot even begin to propagate the vast number of species that make up the wonderful diversity required by the marine aquarium hobby. Commercial concerns must be very selective and propagate only the most valuable and popular species that will produce the greatest return on their investment of time and money. Hobbyists, however, can work with whatever species catch our interest, thus through our efforts we can greatly increase the variety of propagated species.

As marine aquarium hobbyists, we have always had a great interest in creating the techniques and technology for captive propagation of marine organisms. The first step is to breed the species of our interest in small numbers in a home based, experimental facility. Once it is shown that a species can be reared, other hobbyists will work at propagation also, and commercial facilities will quickly follow. This is the way things happened with clownfish culture and are now happening with coral culture.

Unlike corals, however, fish, crustacea, and mollusks must first be spawned, reared through a delicate larval stage, and then grown-out into juveniles before they can be distributed to hobbyists. Thus breeding marine fish is not an easy task. It is not technically difficult, that is not in the same way that mastering calculus, building a satellite, doing brain surgery, or becoming an Olympic athlete is difficult, but it does require an investment of time and effort. The learning curve is a bit steeper than gardening or breeding guppies, and the process is somewhat complex when all the necessary factors such as algae and food organism culture, water quality requirements, disease control, and food organism densities are considered, but propagation of a great variety of species is certainly not beyond the skills of an experienced, and dedicated, marine aquarium hobbyist.

My attempt at small scale culture of the orchid dottyback was quite successful. Using the techniques described in this journal, I reared 351 orchid dottybacks, *Pseudochromis fridmani*, well into the juvenile stage in a 20 gallon tank, so the methods I developed in my home based hatchery are quite viable. My success was due in great measure to my past experience with commercial culture of many species of marine tropical fish, but the techniques developed in my little fish room are at the hobbyist's level. No scientific laboratory equipment (except for a dissecting microscope) or commercial hatchery facilities were used. The basic techniques developed and described are applicable to a variety of situations and many different species. I must make a point to tell you, however, that you will find many loose ends in this rearing project, research possibilities that are suggested but were left relatively unexplored. It will take many years, or many hobbyists, and many experiments to follow up on all these unexplored pathways.

I am in the process of writing a book that I hope will help hobbyists to rear a variety of marine fish. Hoo boy, it's going to be a good book. It will have a lot of information, or at least all that I can find, on the species that are, or that might be, possible to spawn and rear in relatively small systems: how to build systems for brood stock and larval culture, how to select and establish brood stock, forced and natural spawning, pelagic and demersal spawners, larval recovery and larval rearing, environmental control in larval rearing tanks, food organism culture, procedures to follow for setting up breeding projects and much more.

But that is not *this* book. *This* book is something quite different. It is the journal of my breeding work with the orchid dottybacks. I wrote it on almost every day of that project. It is everything I did, almost my every thought (you don't want to know all of them)—it is my very existence for over a year, and it documents all the failure and all the success of that project. I am not the first to breed *Pseudochromis fridmani*, Bill Addison at C-Quest in Puerto Rico and Robert Brons (1996) in Israel have both bred this and other species of *Pseudochromis* in commercial hatchery facilities. But my dottyback work was done at home, in a modified bathroom, by only one individual, and so it has a special application to the hobbyist breeder.

I intended to publish the dottyback journal after the major breeding book was finished. (The working title of that book is, incidentally, *Propagation of Marine Tropical Fish Written so that Hobbyists Can Understand and Use It, but Technical Enough so that It Will Also be Useful to Scientists and Commercial Breeders.* OK, so the title needs a little work.) But that book won't be completed till Santa makes his list, so we decided to publish the journal first to make at least some of the basic information available to the hobby at an earlier date. It is not a formal textbook, and you will have to fish (chuckle) for some of the information among musings and scattered comments, but the index will be helpful. It is not designed to convey information in carefully structured, logical, sequential chapters. That will be the structure of the next, more conventional, breeding book. Look at this little book as a journey, however, a journey through the time line of a marine fish breeding project. I hope that my journal will be helpful to you if you make the attempt to rear marine tropical fish, and if you are content to leave this work to other hobbyists, I think you will still find it interesting and worthwhile to vicariously explore this consuming aspect of the marine aquarium hobby.

It is very important for hobbyists to keep a record of their experiences with propagation of marine organisms, and to make that information avaialable to other hobbyists. **The Breeder's Registry**, P.O. Box 255373, Sacramento, CA (http://www.breeders-registry.gen.ca.us/), a nonprofit organization, maintains a database of species propagated by hobbyists and professionals and makes this data available to interested parties. They also publish the Journal of MaquaCulture. Breeding marine hobbyists are encouraged to join the Registry and submit the results of their propagative efforts.

1

Preparations -
Structures and Systems

Approximately 3.5 billion years ago, a spaceship landed on the hot, steamy and lifeless planet Earth. Alien beings, charged with the responsibility of spreading life in the universe, stepped out on the inhospitable surface of this world and cast out the biologically coded seed that would become, in the fullness of time, intelligent life. Of course, that time has not yet come, but we are working toward it with every century of progress. One of these aliens, Weet8ar by name (the 8 is silent), was much enamored with the role that water would play in the evolution of the planet, and so somewhere, deep down in between the code for masochism and the code for Murphy's Law, he inserted a code for the desire to keep and breed aquatic life. This code would become activated in certain, almost intelligent, future life forms, first through casual contact with small glass boxes, water, and fish, and then bloom into an obsession to engineer aquatic life support systems and study, research, and propagate various marine and freshwater life.

All this is fact, of course, it's called Directed Panspermia, just ask Francis and Leslie. I mean how else can one explain why, after 7 years of recovery from a "hands on" marine fish addiction, I would relapse and build a fish room to once again breed marine tropical fish. Actually, since leaving the commercial marine fish hatchery business in 1987, I always wanted to have a small marine fish breeding room, large enough to work with small fish, but not so large that I would be tempted to once again begin commercial production. It would be a little breeding lab that I could quickly wind down to a holding pattern if I wanted to spend more time on another project, or even, if the situation required, dry it out completely for an extended trip or a necessary hiatus from the daily chores of a fish room.

Thus when we built a new house in 1992, I made plans to convert the spare bathroom into a marine fish breeding laboratory. It is a small room, only 7 x 8 feet, with a tiled floor and a 9 foot ceiling. The toilet and bathtub were plumbed, but not installed, and a laundry tub took the place of the typical bathroom sink. OK, for the first year or two it was a storage room; I mean, what do you want, we had just moved! But I made plans; I needed the most tanks and facilities possible for the available space, and so for months I drew plans and figured, and figured and drew plans.

There are some basic requirements for marine fish culture. I know these very well, having designed, built, and operated four hatcheries, large and small, over the last 20 years. These are the basics for a small, experimental hatchery:

1. Brood stock tanks, with the proper environment, water quality, lighting, and substrate to get the fish in a breeding mode.

2. Larval culture tanks, and for a small experimental laboratory situation, they should be large enough to maintain a stable aquatic environment, but still small enough to fit three or four of them into the

system. Also a consideration, large larval tanks require a large amount of food organisms over a short period of time, especially if two or more larval rearing runs overlap. Although I have four, 8 gallon tanks, I think two 5 to 10 gallon tanks and one 15 to 20 gallon tank would be ideal for a small system.

3. Grow-out tanks, large enough to grow out a couple hundred fish when necessary, but not so large that maintenance and feeding would be a chore.

4. Quarantine and treatment tanks, necessary to process new brood stock and to treat any outbreaks of disease or parasites that might occur.

5. Space for food organism culture, including micro algae culture, rotifer culture, and brine shrimp hatching.

6. A reservoir for saltwater manufacture and storage.

7. A small counter just off a deep sink for wet work.

8. A table for microscope and lab work.

9. A small section of the refrigerator and freezer for foods, vitamins, and other stuff that must be kept cold.

10. Shelves and drawers for storage of gear, medications, foods and equipment.

11. More shelves and drawers for storage of gear, medications, foods, books, and equipment. (It's very important to have places to store all the stuff that you should throw out, but can't because you just might need it someday, if you could only remember where you put it. And, of course, one can never have too many books.)

This is a lot to squeeze into an 7 by 8 foot converted bathroom, and I admit, I didn't quite make it. The reservoir tank for saltwater and the dry work table are in the adjoining spare bedroom, along with a few extra shelves.

I wound up with 1 thirty gallon and 4 twenty gallon brood stock tanks and 4 eight gallon larval rearing tanks, plus a 10 gallon header tank and a 20 gallon sump tank on one central system. The grow-out consists of a 50 gallon tank on a separate system with a second 50 gallon tank as the sump to that system. The algae and rotifer culture and a small area for hatching brine shrimp cysts, are on two wide 6 foot long shelves built over the grow out system. There is also room on two shelves for two 20 gallon quarantine and/or treatment tanks, to process new brood stock and, if necessary, treat fish that have developed a protozoan parasite. The back wall of the room near the door contains, yes, shelves and drawers.

The shelving for all the systems is built from 2 by 3 inch lumber and half inch outdoor grade plywood, all painted white. The 2 by 3's are plenty strong enough, especially when the 3 inch dimension is used for self support, and saves considerable space over the typical 2 by 4 inch construction studs.

The brood stock/larval tank set up is a sump based, gravity flow system, which works very well. The header tank on the top shelf receives all the water from the sump tank pump, except for a small amount that supplies the protein skimmer. A one inch pipe, opening into the bottom of the header tank, distributes the water downward. Horizontal half inch pipes extend outward from the down pipe and provide water to each tank through a valve to regulate flow. The drain system begins with a one inch overflow pipe that sets the water level in the header tank. This drain pipe collects water from the standpipe drains of each tank and then empties into the mechanical filter pad over the sump tank. The pump must provide enough water at an 8 foot head to supply all the tanks with enough extra flow to maintain the water level at the top of the overflow pipe. This way the gravity head on the system is constant regardless of the amount of flow to any tank.

The sump tank, 30 gallon total capacity, is filled about half full and has enough extra capacity to hold the volume of the header tank and all the extra "working water" in the system that might drain if the pump ceases to operate. Two marks on the side of the sump tank indicate the normal working level and the level where water lost to evaporation must be replaced. The water pump is, of course, on the bottom shelf next to the sump tank. The pump is suspended about an inch above the bottom shelf on brass (no rust) chains which makes it very easy to change out the pump and greatly reduces vibration and accumulation of saltwater around the pump.

Since the system contains a relatively light bio-load, biological filtration is easily supplied by the live rock in all the brood stock tanks, and live sand in a few containers in the sump and on the bottom of a few of the tanks. There is a mechanical filter in the form of a felt filter pad under the discharge into the sump. This pad clogs with algae and detritus every few days (and also begins to support a nice population of amphipods), and I hose it off with one of those "sidewalk sweeper" nozzles on the garden hose. The high pressure stream penetrates the filter felt and cleans it nicely. I have two of these pads for each system and I clean and rotate them every few days.

A protein skimmer and a separate activated carbon device is also located in the sump and this completes the filtration on this system. (The protein skimmer and the activated carbon device are of my own design and fabrication and work extremely well, more on this later.) Evaporation is considerable, what with the fan nearby in the doorway, and I add three or four gallons to both the brood stock/larval rearing system and the grow-out system about every three or four days.

The grow-out system has the same filtration arrangement, but is much simpler in construction since it consists of only two tanks. The bottom tank acts as the sump, a submersible pump pushes water up to the top tank, which is distributed along the bottom of the tank at the opposite end of the stand pipe drain. A small "weep hole" in the supply pipe at the surface of water provides a siphon break if and when the electric goes off or the pump fails. Interestingly, I built the two 50 gallon tanks that make up the grow-out system in the summer of 1972, and they first served as the brood stock tanks for the first four pairs of clownfish, *Amphiprion ocellaris*, that I spawned in St. Petersburg, FL, which started this whole thing. They were later clownfish brood stock tanks for 10 years in the Keys hatchery, and then, after 10 years in storage, I put them back into service once again in my home based hatchery.

There is no heating or cooling and the temperature of the systems is regulated by the room temperature. The room is under the central air conditioning of the house and temperature variation during the extremes of winter and summer is not very great, after all this is Ft. Lauderdale, Florida. The room runs warmer than I had anticipated, since the A/C does not have a large outlet in this small room, and a fan in the door helps keep the temperature only about a degree or two F above the house temperature. Thus the tank temperatures run about 80 to 83 °F most of the year. On very cold days, I turn off the fan and close the "bathroom" door, which raises the temperature a few degrees. The tank temperatures may drop into the upper 70's on some winter days when a cold front blows through, but cold temperatures have never been a problem. Actually, the times when it is most difficult to keep temperatures in the proper range are in spring and fall when outside temperatures are close to 80 °F and the A/C does not run often enough to keep that room cool. The solution in these instances is to open the window and allow some of the heat build up to escape.

The brood stock/larval system also has a UV sterilization unit on the water flow up to the header tank, which imposes a "sterile barrier" between each brood stock and larval rearing tank. The UV sterilizer is mounted vertically on the 2 x 3 vertical shelf supports. This was an after construction "add on" since I thought that I could prevent any parasite problems through careful quarantine and treatment of new fish. The quarantine system failed and I had parasite problems. It failed because I was not strict enough in my quarantine procedures and because I used wild plankton in my breeding work without the precaution of treating it with a weak copper solution for an hour or so before sorting. Thus I was forced to implement UV sterilization on the system to put a protective microorganism barrier between the tanks, which is actually a good form of insurance.

Well, by now you are probably totally confused as to the layout, construction, and operation of my little hatchery room. So I have provided a couple of drawings that may give you a better idea of the layout and function of these systems.

A 40 gallon plastic reservoir is located on a table just outside the door of the fish room with a bulkhead drain connected to a half inch hose that reaches all the lower sump tanks in the fish room. A valve on the end of the hose allows precise control of water flow without a drop ever spilling on the floor. (See the Appendix for an idiot proof method of

never forgetting that a tank is filling.) Saltwater is made up
as needed in the reservoir and it is used to fill jars, tanks,
buckets, and the sump tanks of each system. A pipe from the
distribution line of the breeding system extends to the sink

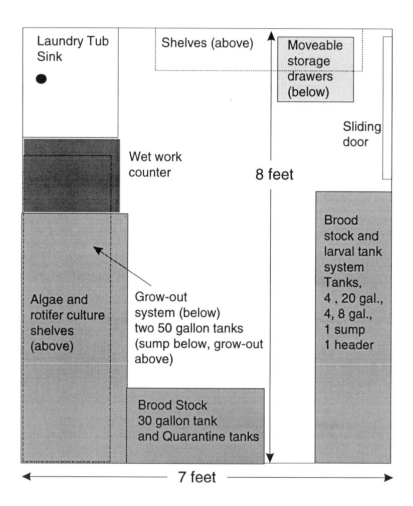

Breeding Room Layout, Top View

so that I can pull saltwater from that system for other purposes such as brine shrimp culture, or just discharge old water into the sink during a water change.

The brood stock tanks, the larval rearing tanks, and the header tank all have plastic covers to reduce evaporation and salt creep, and to prevent fish from jumping out of the tanks. Each tank also has a gentle air release. The air release in each tank keeps the tank water in circulation, reduces the need for extensive water exchange (each tank receives between 0.50 and 0.75 gpm (gallons per minute), about 7 to 12 tank volume exchanges per day), and provides a back up for water pump failure. If the water pump happens to fail, then the air release in each tank keeps everybody alive, and conversely, if the air pump fails, then the water flow maintains life. And if we have a hurricane and the electric is off for a week or two, I have a gas generator that will supply enough current to keep the room in operation for an extended period.

Live rock provides ample biological filtration, and the protein skimmer pulls out a lot of dissolved organic compounds and small detritus particles before they can break down into nutrients. The 100 micron felt filter pad removes most of the larger detritus particles. I have to siphon out detritus build up in each tank every few months, and clean the tank covers occasionally, but the maintenance requirement is not excessive. Granular activated carbon is also used to reduce dissolved organic compounds and organic dyes. Water changes are irregular, but probably average about 10% per month in each system. Algae growths on the inside of the front glass have to be cleaned every few days, which is, along with cleaning the filter pads, the most odious of routine maintenance chores.

In operation, the system works very well. The brood stock and larval tanks all have a hole for a 1 inch bulkhead fitting drilled in the bottom and a standpipe in each tank regulates the water level in the tank. The gravity flow to each tank allows precise regulation of water flow into that tank without any effect on the established flow rates into every other tank. Thus I can open a valve wide to fill a tank, or shut off the flow to a tank completely for treatment or cleaning, and every other tank on the system maintains it's established set flow, whether it is a drip exchange or a major inflow.

Spawning takes place in the 20 (or 30) gallon brood stock tanks. Since this is a system designed for experimental work and not a "save every larvae at every spawn" commercial system, I don't have to include devices and methods for automatic egg and/or larval recovery. The 20 gallon tanks are small enough so that egg and larval dispersal is not extensive and more than enough larvae can be collected for experimental rearing. On the night of hatch, I turn off the water flow into the tank an hour or two before hatch or, in the case of a spawn of pelagic eggs, before spawning. The air release into the tank keeps oxygen levels high and no one suffers because the water flow into the tank has ceased.

Hatching occurs while I am reading the classics (or watching TV), and about 10 to 11:00 PM, I go into the darkened fish room to collect the larvae. A flashlight in the corner of the tank concentrates the dottyback or clownfish larvae and it is an easy task to siphon the larvae into the larval tanks or into a gallon jar if I want to transport them to a remote rearing tank. The larval tanks are located on the shelf below the brood stock tanks (a brilliant plan), which makes transfer of the larvae by siphon a piece of cake. (For those not familiar with American slang, this simply means that it is not at all difficult. One does not have to eat cake while siphoning, in fact, if one were to do so, it might cause problems while starting the siphon).

Lighting is provided by a single four foot full spectrum fluorescent bulb above the upper two 20 gallon brood stock tanks, two 4 foot bulbs over the lower two 20 gallon brood tanks, and a single bulb over the lowest shelf that contains the four 8 gallon larval tanks. The room is very bright, however, because everything is white, the shelves, the walls, the ceiling, and the white tile floor. Also the grow-out tank has 6 four foot fluorescent bulbs over it, which provides much light in the room and grows *Caulerpa* very well. This algal growth gives little fish many hiding places There is one four foot fluorescent bulb over each of the two algae/rotifer shelves that are above the grow-out system. The air pump that supplies air for the needs of the entire room is located on the top shelf of the breeding unit, next to the header tank.

The upper 6 foot shelf of the algae/rotifer area is 12 inches wide and is used for growing algae in wide mouth, one gallon glass jars. The plastic cap of the jars has a single eighth inch hole drilled through it to allow insertion of a length of ridged air tubing. An air stone is not needed in the algae culture jars, bubbles from the open tubing move the culture water quite adequately and the tubing is easy to clean. The plastic cap prevents spray and salt creep from leaving the jars. Wide mouth jars are best because you can get your whole hand into the jar to scrub it and a little chlorine or weak acid will get it even cleaner if necessary.

At first I used plastic containers of one to three gallons, old cookie, fruit, and pretzel containers, but it seemed that the algae plated out more on plastic than on glass and glass is easier to clean. I also discovered later that culturing algae is not absolutely necessary, and so this shelf is now used mostly for storage. There is a way that rotifers can be maintained without algae cultures (a secret formula) and this is also detailed in the Appendix.

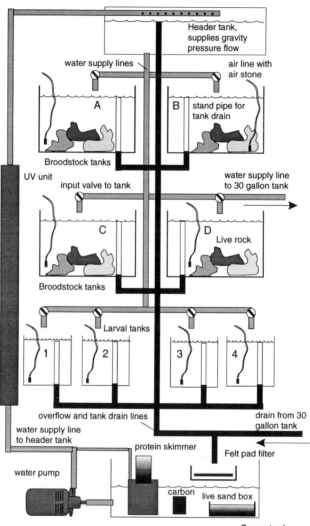

Diagram of the breeding system.

This diagram shows only the elements of water distribution, filtration, and collection. Lighting, shelving, and air pipes were not depicted to avoid confusion. The drawing is not exact to scale, but tank sizes are proportional.

The gray pipes are pressurized water distribution lines and the black pipes are the open overflow and tank drain lines.

The second shelf is 20 inches wide and is used for rotifer culture. Rotifer culture can be done in glass gallon jars also, and these are best for maintaining holding cultures when you don't need vast numbers of rotifers for feeding, but you don't want to lose the cultures and need just to maintain them at relatively low population levels. Tray type food containers that hold up to 5 gallons of culture and measure about 15 by 20 inches and are 4 to 5 inches high, or higher, make good rotifer culture vessels and are easy to clean. Four or five of these trays fit on this shelf, have a thin, clear plastic cover that rests on the top of the trays and has a hole for air tubing. An air stone is best used in these trays since this provides a better flow of air into the water without formation of large bubbles.

A small flat counter by the sink, 15 by 24 inches, provides a space for wet work; a triangular, plastic coated wire shelf in the corner above the sink provides storage for wet work things such as sieves and sponges; and a series of shelves and a moveable stack of drawers on the back wall completes the room. This is a very compact, but quite workable, 7 by 8 foot fish room.

This description of the fish room will give you a good idea of where the work described in the following journal took place, and what equipment and aquarium systems were used to rear the orchid dottybacks. There are many other species of marine fish, such as clownfish, gobies, blennies, cardinalfish, sea horses, comets, and many types of freshwater fish that can be bred in a similar system structure.

Clownfish are now most commonly propagated by marine hobbyists and the techniques to do this have been published in various books and articles. Hoff (1996) has recently published a comprehensive book on the technology developed at Instant Ocean Hatcheries and the history of this commercial clownfish hatchery, and Moe (1989, 1992) discusses rearing marine fish, including clownfish and angel-fish. There are also quite a few magazine articles such as Brosseau (1991), Moe (1989, 1997), Wilkerson (1992), Young (1991), and others that describe rearing marine fish and invertebrates, although most deal with clownfish.

Many of the techniques and methods I used that proved useful in this recent home based dottyback rearing project are detailed in the Appendix, and although they are also buried in the text of the journal, they are more readily available in a separate section. I hope my rearing experiences, as described in this book, will be helpful if you attempt to rear marine fish, and if so, Good Luck to you!

Enjoying the simple pleasures of the fish room

2

February 1996 -
The Journey Begins

These journal entries are, with very few exceptions, exactly the way that they were written on that date. I have kept editing to a minimum to accurately record the concerns and activities at the time of each entry. There is some repetition in these daily accounts, since the work focused on basically the same problems and procedures during the entire 17 month time span of the project. My perspective on the problems, the solutions, and routine activities changes, however, as the project progresses though failure and success, and each revisit to a particular topic usually contains new insights. And of course, the journal also reflects the essential nature of a fish breeding project, the never failing daily accomplishment of the routine chores of food preparation, feeding, and environmental tank maintenance

This journal, however, is not a log book, it is a narrative of the events and progress of the breeding project. A breeder should keep a detailed log book and record every feeding and the accomplishment of every activity, for this is, or can be, very valuable information when problems arise, and they will, trust me on this.

February 2, 1996
Project history

Two tiny, immature, tank reared orchid dottybacks, *Pseudochromis fridmani*, were given to me by Bill Addison of C-Quest at the MACNA convention in Louisville, September 17, 1995. They flew back to Ft. Lauderdale nestled in two little bags between my feet. I placed them in a 20 gallon tank with live rock that contained only a pair of golden cleaner shrimp. In early December of 1995, an immature pair of *A. ocellaris* clownfish was also introduced to that tank. The *P. fridmani* did well during the fall and grew rapidly. Courtship behavior was observed sporadically in the first few weeks of January 1996 and the first spawning was observed on January 20. I estimate the fish were about 6 or 7 months old at first spawning. The location of the spawning was not known at that time because the pair disappeared from sight when not under observation. Later that day the male was observed entering and exiting a particular hole in the rock and I surmised that it was in this hole that the spawning took place. This particular rock has deep, extensive holes created by boring clams. The eggs were not observed at this spawn and no larvae were seen during nightly examinations of the tank.

Active courtship was observed again on January 27, and this time I was able to videotape the entire procedure culminating with the entry of the female into the hole in the rock following the entry of the male. The male approached the female continuously for two or three hours before the spawning and would try to lead her into the hole. He approached the female head to head and would then turn and swim toward the hole while vigorously shaking his tail at the head of the female. She would follow him toward his den only to lose interest as soon as the male disappeared into the hole. She would quickly turn away and swim back toward one corner of the tank. Her abdomen was visibly swollen with hydrating eggs. The male quickly exited the hole when the female did not enter behind him and would begin the enticement process once again. This continued for about two hours before the female finally entered the male's den.

Once both male and female were in the hole, they did not reappear for two hours. A small light shown into the hole revealed both fish side by side engaging in a shaking and fluttering motions. The female was the first to emerge post spawning. She was much thinner and quickly re-treated to the back corner of the tank. The male emerged about 5 to 10 minutes later and re-sumed a "half hearted" attempt at courtship once again. This be-havior gradually lessened. He frequently entered and exited the den over the next 24 hours. With a small flashlight, I could observe the egg mass in the back of the hole. Unfortunately, the male apparently ate the eggs the next day, for after the morning hours, I could no longer see the egg mass in the hole.

Late stage orchid dottyback eggs.

Spawning occurred again on February 2, 1996. The interval between spawnings was 6 days this time instead of the 7 between the first two spawns. This time I removed the egg mass about an hour after spawning. I am attempting to artificially incubate the eggs since they have apparently been lost on the first two spawns when the care was left to the male. The eggs are attached in one mass by profuse, very sticky and very elastic strings that are very thin. In fact, when I first removed the egg mass from the hole with a plastic coated "twistee" wire with a small hook bent into one end, the egg mass reluctantly came out of the hole and then suddenly retracted back into the hole when it became detached from the twistee. The thought that the male had grabbed the egg mass and then retreated back into the hole first entered my mind, but then I realized that the elastic fibers that bound the egg mass were caught inside the den and pulled the eggs back into the hole. At this time, February 3, 10 AM, the eggs are developing nicely, gastrulation has occurred, and the embryo mass is developing to one side of the yolk. Each egg also has a single oil drop. The egg mass is negatively buoyant.

I divided the egg mass into two groups, one group contains about 100 eggs and is held in a jar of system water with three drops of hydrogen peroxide, the other group of about 600 to 800 eggs is held in a blue glass jar in the bottom of the 8 gallon rearing tank with a small flow of water from the system exchange entering the top of the glass. These eggs, the largest group, were initially placed in a 5" long piece of gray PVC pipe with a screen cemented over one end. The purpose of this innovation was to contain the eggs in a dark area, similar to the natural environment, and direct clean, oxygenated water over the eggs. This may be workable, but in this case the valve clogged overnight and water flow was cut off the next morning. The eggs were then removed from the PVC tube and placed in the bottom of the short drinking glass with a slight water flow directed into the top of the glass.

February 4, 1996

Only about 10% of the eggs are still developing. The embryos are now in the free tail stage and pigment is just starting to develop in the eyes (10 AM). I estimate hatching will be perhaps as early as tonight, but possibly tomorrow night. The eggs in the center of the main egg mass suffered the most mortality, perhaps due to the water cut off in the incubation tube the first night. The eggs all around the periphery of the egg mass have the best survival and development. There are many eggs still with live embryos that have not developed well and probably will not be viable at hatch, if they develop that far. I do, at this point, expect a small number of viable larvae to result from this spawn.

The orchid dottyback egg mass incubating in a glass

February 6, 1996, 10:00 AM

First hatching occurred 4 days after spawning. A few larvae have hatched from the egg mass this morning. The egg mass is mostly composed of dead eggs at this point. The live developing eggs are on the periphery of the egg mass. Most now have well developed eyes and small yolk sacs. A few have hatched. It looks as if most hatching will occur this afternoon or tonight. The eggs in the small masses that are detached from the main mass and held in a glass jar with three or four drops of hydrogen peroxide are also doing well but are a bit behind the main mass of eggs in development. There is a greater variation in rate of development than I would have expected. Some hatching seems to occur as a result of physical stimulation, just as in neon goby eggs.

The larvae are small and clear, no visible pigmentation as the larvae are observed in the tank. There are some white pigment spots near the tail on the larvae that are still in the eggs.

February 8, 1996

About 12 healthy larvae were obtained from the third spawn. They were set up in larval tank #3 yesterday, fed rotifers, and as of this afternoon, 4 PM, appear to be feeding and behaving normally. The rotifers are fairly dense in the rearing tank and I have been adding algae to feed the existing rotifer population rather than adding more rotifers. I have not checked the condition of the larvae under the microscope because there are so few of them and they seem to be doing well.

The pair spawned again today, a 7 day interval since the last spawn. The female appeared ready to spawn yesterday as she was full and had a slightly extended ovipositor. The male, however, made only half hearted attempts to lure her into his nest. Today at about 3 PM they both entered his lair rather quickly. The courtship did not extend for several hours as it did the time before. I have made up an egg tumbler powered by water or air flow to contain the eggs after this spawn. I will break up the egg mass into many small units and tumble them during the entire incubation period.

February 9, 1996, 5:30 PM

There are about 12 larvae in rearing tank #3 from the 2/6 hatch. They are feeding well, and with the 250 power eyeglasses (powerful reading glasses) I can actually see the rotifers in the guts of some of the most active larvae. I may have to do a water change in a day or two. They are still very small and unless the rate of growth speeds up greatly, I think it will be a while before they go on brine shrimp. The eggs from the spawn of 2/8 are tumbling in the peanut butter jar tumbler and they look very good at this point. I have a small number of eggs in a water glass to observe embryonic development (with a few drops of hydrogen peroxide to control bacteria), and from this sample (about 30 eggs) it appears that only about 5% of the eggs were not fertilized. System water flows though the jar and tank and no anti-bacterial methods are in use.

February 12, 1996, 6:00 PM

There are still about 8 to 10 larvae in tank #3 from the 2/6 hatch. Several of the larvae have started to feed on new hatch brine shrimp as of today. A 20 % water change was done yesterday and additional rotifers, enriched with Selco, were also added today. The larvae are about 3 mm long as of this PM.

The spawn of 2/8 is not doing well. A few hatched last night and made their way out of the egg tumbler, so I pulled the eggs from the tumbler and set them up in a water glass. Many of the eyed eggs died in the bottom of the glass even though I had put the air stone in the glass as well. I think I will be lucky to get 10 larvae from this spawn. More should hatch tonight. Rotifers are already added to this tank since I have to leave tomorrow at 5 AM for a two day trip to Cancun.

February 15, 1996

Back from Cancun last night. Great trip, only two days but I got to see some of the city and had a boat trip over to Isles Murhares. It was a consulting trip to help with spiny lobster, *Panulirus argus*, mortality in holding corrals. Never have I seen such huge lobsters in such great numbers. They had 10,000 adult Caribbean spiny lobsters in a pen

One of thousands of monster spiny lobster taken off the coast of the Yucatan peninsula

only about 60 feet long and 30 feet wide. There was excellent water flow though the pens, and in my opinion, the lobster mortality was caused by keeping the lobsters out of water after capture and during transport for too long a time, up to 5 hours cumulative, for some lobsters before they were placed back in the water.

The *P. fridmani* spawned again yesterday (Wed. 2/14). This time the male kept the eggs until I removed them at about 12 PM today. I split the egg mass and replaced half with the male and incubated the remainder with antibiotics. The eggs were with the male for almost 24 hours and developed very well. All the embryos were at the same point in development (the free tail stage, quite advanced) and very few showed no development. Also no sign of bacterial decay or embryo death after development began. The embryos were far more advanced and much stronger then when the eggs were artificially incubated.

A few larvae, about 3 or 4, from the 2/6 hatch are still doing well at 10 days old. They seem to be feeding more on rotifers than on new hatch brine shrimp. Perhaps they require the very smallest napulii of the brine shrimp. I suspect that when the brine shrimp get a few days old, they outgrow the feeding capabilities of the young fish larvae. There are also a few larvae from the hatch of 2/12, about 3. They seem to be feeding on rotifers and doing well at this point.

February 16, 1996, 9:00 AM

The artificially incubated eggs seem to be doing well. There is some breakdown of developed eggs but only about 10%. The male is still incubating half of the egg mass. Although I am tempted, I have not removed the eggs he is holding to see how they are developing. The arti-

ficially incubated eggs are being held in a two gallon fish
bowl with an air release on the bottom to circulate the
water and a dose of old neomycin and oxytetracycline. I
noticed that when an air bubble was trapped in the interior
of the egg mass, the eggs floated and gently circulated
near the top of the bowl. I carefully inserted a small chip of
styrofoam in the egg mass to provide buoyancy when the
air bubble escaped, and the egg mass now floats gently at
the surface of the bowl. The embryos seem to be continuing to develop normally. The eyes are pigmented and there
are strong pigment spots on the posterior sides of the body.

11:00 AM, February 16

BUMMER! The male apparently ate his half of the
eggs. He is now out and swimming about without the very
frequent returns to the hole that were characteristic of yesterday and this morning. I also cannot see the egg mass
within the hole with a small flashlight as I could yesterday
and this morning. My half of the egg mass, however,
seems to be doing fine and I do not intend to eat the eggs
under my care. I suspect that they will hatch tomorrow
night.

February 19, 1996, 11:00 AM

First the good news. There are two larvae left from the
hatch of the 6th, they are 13 days old now and are at the
bottom in one corner of the tank. They feed mostly on rotifers although they seem large enough to feed on new hatch
brine shrimp. I started a trickle change yesterday PM and
now the trickle is down to only drops as the valve clogs a
bit. The water is fairly clear and most of the old food organisms have been washed out. I think at least one full change
has been accomplished. They seem to be doing well and
appear to be actively feeding. The lights have been on only

in the daytime, a normal light dark schedule, the same photoperiod as that for the adults, 12 dark and 12 light with about an hour of subdued light before and after the tank lights are out.

The bad news is that the last spawn, the spawn of 2/14 has almost completely died out. There is one, maybe two larvae alive from this hatch (2/17). The eggs were developing very well even for a day after removal from the nest cared for by the male. The last day they seemed to die from lack of oxygen or stimulation; I don't think that bacteria were the problem. I did use two antibiotics in the incubation tank water, neomycin and oxytetracycline.

The pair spawned again yesterday, 2/18. They spawned in a short section of 3/4 inch gray PVC pipe with a cap on one end. So far I have left the eggs with the male. I don't want him to eat the eggs, they develop very well under his care, but he has eventually eaten every nest that is left with him. I'll pull the eggs as late as I dare.

February 28, 1996

I have to catch up here, no entries for the last 10 days. On the spawn of 2/18, the male ate the eggs on the 20th. The pipe was quite open in that the end of the pipe pointed to the front glass, so I could observe the inside of the pipe very easily. This may have contributed to the stress on the male.

I left for a weekend speaking engagement early on the 23rd and did not return until mid day on the 26th. There was still one larva alive from the 2/6 hatch and one from the hatch of 2/12. When I returned on the 26th, I could not observe any larvae in either tank.

The female was full again and I thought that they might spawn on the 22nd, but they did not. I anticipated a spawn on the 23rd, and when I returned on the 26th, I observed a spawn with well developed embryos that I assume was laid on the 23rd. Since the male had cared for the eggs well from the 23rd to the 26th, I did not remove the spawn and tried not to disturb the male or the nest. I taped a back plastic curtain over the tank in front of the nest entrance to shield the male from activity in the tiny little fish room. I checked once or twice a day to make sure that the eggs remained, but otherwise did not disturb the male or the nest. I could see the egg ball in the back of the hole and observed the even development of all the eggs through the stage of eye pigmentation.

The water temperature was a little high, about 80 to 82 degrees F, so I figured, based on observations of past egg development, that they would hatch on Tuesday night, 2/27. We had a meeting of the Miami Marine Aquarium Society that night, so I set the timer to turn off the lights about an hour later, at 9:15 PM instead of 8 PM. Hatching was in progress when we returned home at about 10:30 PM. The 20 gallon tank was full of tiny larvae, I estimate about 1000 larvae were in the tank. I had turned off the water flow into the tank when we left so only the air stone was providing circulation in the tank. The male had finally done his job for the next generation (I hope) and for my little aquaculture project.

I siphoned a number of larvae into two larval tanks, B and C. One tank, B, was freshly cleaned and filled with 50% system water and 50% new artificial seawater. The other tank, the oldest one, had been set up since 2/4 and had a good growth of algae on the sides and bottom and a strong population of copepods living on this substrate. Since I noticed the larvae of the previous spawn had fed on organisms on the sides of the tank, I changed water in

Larval tanks B and C are prepared for larval rearing with black plastic around each side and one air stone prividing a gentle turbulence

the tank by allowing a flow through of system water, which flushed the tank but did not remove the flora and fauna on the sides and bottom of the tank. I also siphoned larvae into two plastic bottles since there were so many in the tank. There were at least 100 larvae remaining in the tank when I stopped moving them to the other tanks.

Today I will set up the feeding cultures in the larval tanks and begin removing and observing larvae under the microscope to record their development and observe the results of feeding activity, numbers and species of food organisms.

The male began courting the female early this morning, 2/28, and when I observed them at 9:30 AM, they were both in the nest and engaged in spawning activity. Prolific spawners, these orchid dottybacks!

5 PM

The *P. fridmani* larvae started feeding on rotifers about noon. I will have to scramble to get enough rotifers for this batch. I lost 2 cultures over the weekend while I was in Pennsylvania, and the third and only culture I now have is relatively new and I have had to harvest it fairly intensively to get enough to start the larvae out. I started another rotifer culture without waiting for an algal bloom by adding a large inoculation of algae and giving it only a day to start before adding the rotifers. I have also begun two large cultures of algae, 20 and 30 gallons, out on the patio to supply algae and rotifers a week or so down the line when there is, hopefully, another hatch. I have about 250 to 300 larvae in each 8 gallon larval tank so I will need a good quantity of rotifers. I enrich the rotifers with Selcon and Zoe for about 30 minutes after harvest and before feeding. I am also trying to keep some algae in the larval rearing tank to maintain the nutritional value of the rotifers that do not get eaten immediately.

3

March 1996 -

Death and Disaster

March 1, 1996

Yesterday was a big day. Not only was it Leap Year day, Feb. 29, but it was also a big breakthrough in rearing the *P. fridmani.* I fed the larvae enriched rotifers in the morning, about 10 AM. I removed a larva shortly after and examined it under the dissecting microscope. There were many rotifers in the gut and the larva seemed to be growing well. I noticed that the mouth seemed quite large for such a small larva, even though the head was pointed and the mouth seemed small, when I examined it with dissecting needles I observed that the mouth actually opened very wide and that it seemed large enough to accept a newly hatched brine shrimp.

Newly hatched brine shrimp, especially the San Francisco brine shrimp, have a first nauplius stage that is quite small and can be taken by a relatively small larva. After only a few hours, however, the first molt takes place and the nauplius gains enough in size that it is no longer acceptable to the small larvae. I added new hatch brine shrimp, which I had set up the previous afternoon and soon observed two day old *P. fridmani* larvae with orange guts, a sure sign of ingestion of brine shrimp nauplii. I caught and dissected one larva and confirmed the presence of brine shrimp napulii in the gut. This was nothing short of astounding, feeding on brine shrimp at two days in a larval fish as small at hatch as the *P. fridmani*. They fed on brine shrimp all during the day.

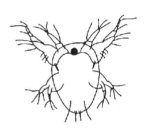

Brine shimp napulii.

The next day, today - March 1, I noted that the brine shrimp remaining in the larval tank from the previous day were too large to be taken by the fish larvae. They would assume the typical feeding stance, an S shaped curve just in front of the prey organism, but would not strike. I added rotifers, which were now very scarce in the tank and observed the larval fish begin feeding on them. Fish larvae that do not feed on any food organism are transparent and small. There is little chance that these larvae will survive and too many of such larvae early in the rearing run indicate that the run will be a failure. Fish larvae that feed on rotifers or copepods have dense white guts and are easily seen in the tank. As soon as they begin to feed on brine shrimp napulii, the guts become orange, a very distinct change in appearance.

About 10 AM I harvested the brine shrimp that I had set up the day before and the larval *P. fridmani* quickly began feeding once again on the newly hatched brine shrimp. I can actually see the larvae select the new hatch brine and pass over the day old brine shrimp. The new hatch brine shrimp are very orange and appear as a tiny dense orange spot where the day old brine shrimp are less

A brine shrimp hatchery made from a 2 liter soda bottle. Rigid air tubing extends to the bottom of the bottle. No air stone is necessary and a wad of filter floss in the bottle neck contains salt spray within the bottle.

intense in color, larger, swim faster and one can see the movement of the developing swimmerets.

The rotifer cultures are holding out, but I have only two trays of culture and they do not have much of a chance to recover after each morning's harvest. The algae cultures are not coming up quickly. I fear that I will be hard pressed to culture enough rotifers in the days ahead, especially if the male has learned how to incubate the eggs.

The next spawn, that so far he has taken good care of, should hatch on Sunday night, March 3rd. This would be an incubation of 4 days, the same as with the last spawn.

The 20 and 30 gallon cultures are starting to come up outside, but there is a cold front coming in two days and this might knock them back considerably. I may inoculate rotifer tray # 2 with rotifers this PM if the bloom comes up a bit more. I like to get the algae bloom very dark before I inoculate with rotifers since this produces a strong rotifer culture very quickly, but in this case I need the rotifers very soon and I would rather have a weak culture coming up than no rotifers at all.

March 2, 1996, 4:30 PM

This is day 4 for the *P. fridmani* larvae. There seemed to be a loss in numbers this AM, but this is a very subjective observation. When the guts are empty and the larvae are spread out in the tanks it is very difficult to get a feel for how many are present. Even when there are food organisms in the guts, the spread of the larvae in the areas where the background is dark makes it difficult to see how many are present. There are still significant numbers in each tank, possibly 50 to 60 in the new tank (B) and perhaps 100 in the old tank (C). The larvae in the tank with algae on the sides, some detritus, and a copepod population, seem to be doing a bit better than those in the clean tank. They seem more active, perhaps a bit bigger and more numerous. Because of this observation, I have set up a 10 gallon tank and the remaining larval tank (D) with some live sand on the bottom of the tank in preparation for the hatch tomorrow night. The male is still taking good care of the eggs from the spawn of 28 Feb., so I anticipate a hatch on Sunday night, 3 March.

The outside tanks have not come up with an algae bloom yet. I was hoping for a quick bloom out there, but the regular algae cultures in the fish room are finally starting to bloom. I harvested the rotifer cultures only once today, I need to have as strong a rotifer culture as possible on Monday for the new hatch. The larvae are now feeding on new hatch brine very actively. I have added the new brine three times today and each time the guts have turned orange. Unfortunately, they do not consume all the new hatch brine shrimp and the shrimp soon outgrow the larval fish's ability to feed on them. Thus the tanks are becoming heavy with one and two day old brine shrimp. It would be far better for the culture if I could remove these older brine shrimp, but I can't pull them out without also removing the fish larvae. I did change abut 10 to 15% of the water in the new tank (B) today with a trickle flow and window screening (1 mm or 1000 micron mesh) over the outlet just to try to pull out the older brine shrimp. This worked to some extent, only a few larvae were lost, but it also took out the new hatch brine shrimp and the rotifers. I will try this again in a day or two when the fish larvae are larger and better able to escape the pull of the water flow.

March 3, 1996,1:30 PM

The outside tanks are a bust so far. It doesn't look as if there will be an algal bloom anytime soon. Rotifers are still very scarce and there should be a hatch tonight of the *P. fridmani*. The larvae in tanks B and C are still doing well. Tank C, the "old" tank, is significantly better in that the larvae are more numerous, larger and more active. I changed some water and tried to pull out the large brine shrimp napulii in both tanks this morning. I used a plastic needlepoint mesh (about 2 mm) inserted into the cut out top of a plastic peanut butter jar, to siphon water and brine shrimp nauplii from the tank from an area where larval fish were not present. It worked to a great extent, but there are still too many large brine shrimp in each tank. I think the solution is to feed more strongly on the rotifers and phase in the brine shrimp napulii more slowly so that they are available, but do not overrun the tank. This will require more rotifers than I now have in culture. I estimate that there are about 50 larvae in tank C and about 30 larvae in tank B as of this afternoon. Most mortality seems to occur overnight. The larval tanks are on the same day night cycle as the brood stock tanks. I would like to try constant light on one run to see if this lowers the early mortality.

March 5, 7:30 PM

The spawn of 28 Feb. hatched on the night of March 3, as expected. There were a few early hatchlings on the night of March 2, but only a few. I set up the hatch of March 3 in two tanks, the 8 gallon larval tank D and a 10 gallon tank set up in the middle of the larval rearing room. Because of the significantly better survival of the previous spawn in Tank C, the "old" tank, which indicated, to me, that the bacterial population was better suited for survival of the larvae, I put about a quarter inch of live sand from the filters on the bottoms of both new larval tanks. I will continue to try the "probiotic" approach, but also work with antibiotics as well. The hatchlings were siphoned from the brood stock tank directly into both larval tanks. I set up a light over the 10 gallon tank and I will leave this light on constantly throughout this run in this tank. The light over larval tank D will be on the same schedule as the brood stock and other larval tanks.

The new larvae were fed rotifers about noon the day after hatch, March 4, and some new hatch brine shrimp on the next day, today, March 5. They seemed to take the rotifers and then the brine shrimp avidly. Strong feeders in other words. So far mortality in both new larval tanks is slight.

Troubles in the old tanks! The larvae in tanks B and C have suffered great mortality. Most of the mortality occurs at night, and every morning over the last two or three days there has been a significant drop in numbers. At this time, March 5 (Day 7 of the run), there are only about 5 larvae in Tank B and about 15 in tank C. The old tank did much better in the numbers, growth and vitality of the larvae, but this is still nothing to shout about. I am going to have to try antibiotics on the next few runs. I don't have much to work with in the way of antibiotics. I need to get some streptomycin as soon as possible.

Troubles also with the algae and rotifer cultures. The rotifers are dependent on the growth of large amounts of microalgae. The *T-Isochrysis* that I am working with is very touchy, it comes up fine in one container and crashes in another set up exactly the same way. And without the algae, the rotifer cultures die out. I may have to go with plastic bag cultures and perhaps another type of alga.

At this point, I think I will be lucky to bring through a half dozen larvae from the Feb. 27 hatch.

March 6, 1996, 10:30 AM

Still having problems with algae culture. Only about one out of three cultures come up with a dense algal bloom. I have had to resort to a little bit of yeast in the rotifer cultures to maintain the little beasts. There are still enough rotifers to feed the new spawn, Tanks D and the 10 gallon temporary set up. These fish are doing well so far, not much mortality in either tank. The light on the 10 gallon tank is constant, no dark period, and the larvae seem to be about the same as the ones in tank D. They are both taking new hatch brine, but it has to be real new hatch, before the first molt of the napulii, or the larvae will not take them. I added a bit of Furnace to Tank D and I will add 200 mg Neomycin to the 10 gallon tank. I hope that the these antibiotics will limit the development of bacterial toxins. The Neomycin is old, however, and may not be very effective. I have also limited my heavy hand with the brine shrimp in the new tanks to try to reduce the "old brine shrimp" problem in the days ahead.

The larvae are almost gone from tank B. Setting up a new clean tank and running it without antibiotics did not result in a successful run. Tank C, the tank with the old

Rotifer culture tanks outside on the patio, protected from rain and intense sunlight

growth and the small population of copepods has done
much better. Perhaps this is a case of "probiotics", the establishment of populations of "good" bacteria in the culture environment before the introduction of the larvae. The
larvae are 8 days old now and about 12 remain. They are
feeding well on new brine shrimp and are beginning to ori-
ent to the corners, sides, and bottom of the tank. They have
not yet begun to develop coloration. I am resisting the
temptation to pull one out and dissect it. I may later, but if
I do, that one would be the one that would have survived.
A trickle change yesterday cleared most of the old brine
shrimp from the tank. I am still hopeful of bringing some
through.

The male is still caring for the eggs. If all goes well they
should hatch tomorrow night. But where to put them? I
think I'll put a heavy water change on tank B, since there
are only one or two larvae left in that tank, add a little live
sand to the bottom, and put them in that tank. With luck,
I'll find an effective antibiotic in time for this hatch that
will allow them to survive in these small tanks.

March 8, 1996, 6:00 PM

The algae cultures are blooming again. The two outside tanks are getting dark at last, I will inoculate them
with rotifers tomorrow. I have two good algae cultures inside also but they are not yet dense enough to feed to the
rotifer cultures. I have kept the rotifer cultures going with
yeast, but this does not produce the best rotifers. I rou-
tinely enrich the rotifers with Selco for 15 to 30 minutes before feeding them to the larvae. Sometimes I also add a few
drops of a marine aquarium vitamin supplement.

The hatch in the old tank, C, is 10 days old now and
only about 5 remain. They seem to be feeding and they are

hanging near the bottom in the corner of the tank. They are still without color. I hope a few make it through to the juvenile stage. I have given them a water change of about 1/3 to 1/2 twice in the last 4 days.

The hatch of 3/3 is 5 days old today. I added streptomycin (I found a source yesterday and it was shipped overnight) to both tank D and the 10 gallon tank in addition to the furnace and neomycin that was put in these tanks, respectively, a few days ago. There are still many larvae in both tanks, although there has been mortality, perhaps 50 percent. I was reading my old notes from the Gray and French Angelfish rearing of 1977 and I had noted that there was a very dramatic difference in the survival of tanks of larval angelfish after I began to use the streptomycin. So we shall see...

The spawn of 3/3 hatched on 3/7, yesterday, right on the four day schedule that incubation has been following. I set up the larvae in larval tank B, that I had cleaned that day. I added about 500 mg of streptomycin, which is roughly 50 mg per gallon, this morning after feeding rotifers. So far the larvae look good, no mortality yet that could be ascribed to the antibiotic treatment.

March 9, 1996, 11:15 AM

There are only 2 to 3 larvae left in "old" tank C. One of the problems may be a population of amphipods in algal growths at the bottom of the tank. These amphipods will take large brine shrimp so they may have also been preying on the larval *P. fridmanis* during the last week. I don't think that this is the reason for the die off in this tank, however. The few remaining larvae are now 10 days old and the drop off is typical of past rearing runs. I will probably remove any survivors next Thursday and prepare that tank for the Thursday night hatch.

The hatch of 3/3 is now 6 days old. Accumulation of large brine shrimp is a major problem in tank D and the 10 gallon tank. The larvae feed avidly on the very new hatch brine shrimp, but as soon as they make that first molt, the larval *P. fridmani* do not take them and they accumulate in the tank. More new hatch brine must be added once or twice per day to keep the guts full. I hope the streptomycin will act as it did with the angelfish and allow the larvae to grow rapidly, if so, this will (should) help with this problem. I noted empty guts in the larvae in these tanks before the feeding of new hatch brine shrimp and full guts shortly after feeding. I was able to remove some of the excess brine shrimp from each of these tanks by cutting off the air release, waiting until the brine shrimp gathered at the surface, and then carefully skimming the surface with a small cup. The few *P. fridmani* larvae that were captured were returned to the tank with an eyedropper.

The latest hatch, 3/7, does not have a great many larvae. One reason is that I siphoned the larvae into an already full tank so that the tank overflowed during the larval siphoning process. A number of larvae were undoubtedly lost down the drain during the siphoning. There are about 100, however, and they seem to be doing very well so far. They are feeding on rotifers; I added a very few new hatch brine shrimp (NHBS) about 10:30, a little early, but only a very few NHBS were added. I will try to add only what they can eat of NHBS over the next few days and thus keep the brine shrimp populations as low as possible.

I added rotifers to the outside 30 gal algae tank. Temperatures dropped to about 50 degrees last night (and

that's really cold down here) so I am not sure that this inoculation will take, but I can add more rotifers later after
temperatures warm up.

March 11, 1996, 11:00 AM

Discouragement! There are no larvae, at least none that
I could find, left in tank C. They lasted for 11 days before
the last one was gone in this run. The run of 3/3 is also, for
all practical purposes, gone. A few remain in tank D and in
the 10 gallon tank, but they do not look at all well and I
doubt that any will make it. The larvae from the last run in
Tank B, now into day 4, look very good (but they all did at
this day). They are feeding almost exclusively on rotifers
yet; I have added a very few new hatch brine shrimp and
they have taken most of them. I am trying to maintain
them more strongly on rotifers for a longer period of time
before making a switch to brine shrimp. I think perhaps
that the scarcity of good rotifers I have been experiencing,
due to the constant crashing of the *T-Isochrysis* cultures,
has pushed me to rely more on brine shrimp in the very
early days of the culture than I should. I will try with this
run and the next run due to hatch tomorrow, to put off the
greater brine shrimp feeding until day 6 or so. This run,
tank B, is also the first run that will have the streptomycin
starting at day 1, which may make a difference.

I am also going to clean the two larval tanks that I will
use on the next run, tanks C and D, very well and use new
saltwater to start the tanks, except for whatever system
water that will be siphoned in with the larvae.

March 12, 1996, 6:10 PM

Encouragement! The larvae in tank B, the run that
started with the hatch on 3/7, is in day 5 and they look

very good. There are quite a few remaining, more than 50, and they are feeding very well. I have fed heavily with rotifers and sparingly with new hatch brine shrimp. The tank is not thick with brine shrimp at this point, a change from previous runs. The larvae also seem more active at this point, but this is a very subjective observation.

There are a few larvae that remain in the 10 gallon tank. They are active and feeding well at day 9, but there are only a very few, less then 10, remaining.

There is a hatch due tonight, however, the tank temperatures have been lower than usual, 77 to 79 degrees F. The usual temps are in the 79 to 82 range. Therefore it is possible that the hatch will be delayed for a day, but I doubt it. I have prepared tanks C and D, by cleaning them out and adding about 4 gallons each of new mix artificial sea water. I will siphon the hatch into these tanks as usual and thus mix some system water in with the new saltwater, probably about a 50 - 50 mix.

March 13, 1996, 11:00 AM

Complications! In the same tank that I keep the breeding pair of *P. fridmani*, I have a pair of "Golden cleaner shrimp", *Stenopus* sp., an undescribed species (unless they are the same species as *S. spinosus*, from the Mediterranean, which I doubt) from the northern Gulf of Mexico. They were collected off Destin, Florida by David Smith. They have been spawning on and off for the last 6 months and my attempts to rear the larvae have not been successful. I have only been able to get them to day 24. Although they have grown well, the rearing runs have experienced increasing mortality and eventually dying out without the larvae going through metamorphosis. As luck would have it, the last spawn of these shrimp came off last night at the same time that the *P. fridmani* hatched. The newly hatched larvae were mixed in the tank together. I had no choice but to put both spawns into the two larval tanks, C and D, that I had prepared. Both spawns are alive and well in these tanks this morning. I fed enriched rotifers to both tanks and put 500 mg of streptomycin in both tanks.

I have heard from Syd Kraul that some of the ornamental shrimp he has reared fed actively on fish larvae during the larval stage. Well, we will see what happens in these tanks. Tank C had a much higher density of larvae then tank D. I siphoned into tank C first, so it must have gotten the most dense concentration of larvae. There are about 300 larvae in tank C, and only about 100 in tank D, give or take a hundred or so (OK, so I'm not too confident on my numerical estimates of the tiny little dots of life in these tanks.) The fish larvae are tiny little icicles of life darting about the tanks while the ponderous shrimp larvae hang quietly in small groups and move slowly through the noisy little fish.

The *P. fridmani* larvae in tank B are still doing well this morning. They are in day 6 and are still vigorous and feeding well. Mortality seems to have leveled off and there are about 30 (?) left at this point. Feeding is still mainly rotifers, although I will step up the new hatch brine shrimp a bit today.

March 14, 1996, 5:30 PM

The *P. fridmani* larvae in tank B are still doing well. They are in day 7 today, and there has been some mortality. There are still many in the tank, however, perhaps 20. They are feeding well on new hatch brine shrimp and rotifers. I feed the rotifers first and about a half hour later feed the brine shrimp. I also added another small dose, about 300 mg, of streptomycin.

The shrimp and fish larvae in tanks C and D seem to be doing well. They are feeding on rotifers, only a few brine shrimp have been added. I have seen no shrimp feeding on fish up to this point.

I have to go on a 3 day trip leaving tomorrow noon. My daughter, Andrea, will come in and feed once on Saturday. I will have to keep my fingers crossed.

March 15, 1996, 11:15 AM

Leaving in a few minutes for the Tampa trade show. All is set up in the breeding room for the trip, hopefully there will be a few left when we return. *P. fridmani* should not be this hard to rear! They do wonderfully well for the first 5 or 6 days. They feed the day of hatch on rotifers and pick up on brine shrimp napulii within a day or two. They just seem to stop growing and feeding on about day 7 or so, although some do continue feeding for a few more days; then they seem to all die out by about day 12. It has to be either water quality, a nutritional problem, or a bacterial toxin.

The 10 gallon tank larvae were 12 days old today, only one remained. He seemed to be in good shape although not feeding very strongly, I transferred him to tank B. The larvae in Tank B are still strong at day 8. They are still numerous, although mortality is still progressing, I estimate about 20 remain at this point, and are feeding well on new brine shrimp and rotifers.

The latest spawn, the mixed shrimp and fish larvae, are doing very well. I did see a shrimp feeding on a fish larvae today, but both shrimp and fish seem to be feeding well on the rotifers and brine shrimp. Mortality up to today, day 3, has been slight in both species.

March 18, 1996, 3:30 PM

Returned from the Tampa trade show last night at 9 PM. The lights on the algae cultures were still on, so no hatch had occurred. I checked the hole with a flashlight and the male was still curled up around a ball of eggs. The light reflected off the silver eyes of the embryos still encased in the eggs. The hatch came off about 45 minutes after the lights in the room went out. I had wanted to watch the hatch and see the larval fish come out of the rock but it occurred very quickly during the 10 minutes that I was away from the fish room. This hatch was set up in the 10 gallon tank. Streptomycin and rotifers were added this morning and the larvae are feeding on rotifers at this time. I sampled the larvae, examined the gut contents and found about 4 or 5 rotifers in each gut.

The larvae in Tank B are 11 days old now and there are about 6 to 8 left in the tank. There was considerable mortality over the weekend. Andrea, my daughter, fed the larvae once a day on Saturday and Sunday and I doubt that survival would have been any greater had I been here those two days. These larvae are looking good and are feeding actively. It seems that they are feeding more on rotifers than brine shrimp, but this is difficult to determine without dissecting one or two larvae and I don't want to reduce the chances of some survival by sampling the larvae.

The mixed hatch of cleaner shrimp and *P. fridmani* are still going. Interestingly, the shrimp larvae have almost completely died out. There are only a few shrimp larvae remaining in Tank C, about 10 ?, and fewer than this in Tank D, and these are apparently feeding on brine shrimp napulii, at least the guts appear to be orange. The fish larvae are feeding on both rotifers and brine shrimp napulii. The fish larvae are numerous in tank C and sparse in Tank D. But then there were only a relatively few larvae placed in Tank D initially.

I am going to have to do more work with enrichment techniques. I heard at the trade show that Selco and Super Selco were more concentrated than the Selcon that I have been using. Also, a lot more attention is now being directed at the complex of various fatty acids rather than the amount of Omega 3, for example. Frank Hoff said that he would send me some of the Super Selco, so I will try it and see if it makes a difference.

March 19, 1996, 1:30 PM

It is puzzling. There are only 2 larvae left in the oldest tank. They are 12 days old today. Yesterday there were about 6 and they all looked good, feeding and moving around, no drifting, no empty guts. There were no indications that such mortality would take place overnight. The two remaining larvae are strong and feeding well today. There is something critical missing from my rearing technique with *P. fridmani.*

3:30 PM, Oops, Took a good look in this tank and there are actually 5 larvae remaining and they are feeding well and are strong and active.

The larvae in Tank B and C are also strong. There are a few shrimp left and they are feeding well. The larvae look strong and active, as usual, at this point.

The last hatch is 2 days old today, mortality is slight, they are feeding well on rotifers and I have added a few new hatch brine shrimp, which many of the larvae have been feeding upon. I have also added a little iodine, which may be helpful.

The pair of *P. fridmani* have spawned again today, this time in the morning, perhaps because they did not spawn yesterday, the day after the hatch, as I had expected. Perhaps they are beginning to slow down, or perhaps the one day lapse was because they were not fed well over the weekend. At any rate, they have a nice egg ball in the nest which should hatch in four days, Sat. 3/23.

March 20, 1996, 4:30 PM

Not much time right now for notes. Only two larvae left in tank B. They are 13 days old today. The two that I have been able to see are strong and active and feeding well. I have no idea what happened to the other 3 that I observed yesterday. The other larval tanks are doing well. Some mortality has occurred but there are many strong and active larvae in all the other larval tanks, C, D, and the 10 gallon tank.

March 22, 1996, 1:00 PM

It has been cold, high of 65 F, for several days now. The outside cultures are in crash state and the inside cultures are very slow to come up. There are few good rotifers and I am feeding them with yeast and various micron sized "invertebrate" foods. I will not do much better with the fridmani's until I get better food cultures going. I have ordered *Nanochloropsus* from Frank Hoff and also some Super Selco so I hope that in the not too distant future I will have better rotifer cultures going. All part of the learning curve, I guess.

There is at least one larva left in Tank B. He is large and strong and active, and if the gods are with me, he may make it through. He is 15 days old today. The larvae in the other tanks are suffering for lack of good nutrition. I doubt that I will get any through in these tanks. There are still a few shrimp larvae remaining and quite a few fish larvae in these 10 day old tanks as well. Many good larvae are also in the 5 day old tanks, but I'm afraid that their nutritional history is not very good.

March 25, 1996, 4:00 PM

Still struggling. The lone larva in tank B seemed strong and was feeding and active on 3/23. There was a hatch that night and I had no other tanks so I carefully moved the lone larva to tank C, in with the (that day) 11 day old larvae. As of today, day 18 for the loner, I am not sure that he didn't survive, but I also can't be sure that he is still alive, but I doubt it. The larvae in tank C are now 13 days old and some of them are feeding well and are active, but others are drifting and obviously bowing out. I examined one of these larvae and the gut was empty, even though there were rotifers and variously sized brine shrimp in the tank.

They have stopped feeding either because the food was not suitable or nutritious enough or because of some other factor such as bacterial toxins. The tank is carrying a dose of streptomycin so I doubt that it is bacterial toxins. I will work to improve the quantity and nutritional quality of the rotifers before working on the water quality. Right now the *T-isochrysis* algae is about gone. None of the gallon jar cultures are developing. I think I have a super ciliate infestation in the algae, which infects the new cultures that I set up. I will stop using system water for the new cultures with the new algae, when I get the new algae.

There are still a few of the cleaner shrimp larvae in larval Tank C and perhaps Tank D also. There are only a few and they are far less numerous than the fish larvae. Only a few fish larvae still survive in Tank D. They are 13 days old today. The larvae in the 10 gallon tank are still surviving at day 8, but I did not, and still don't, have sufficient rotifers to feed them properly. I anticipate that the remaining larvae in this tank will die out within a few days. Because of the lack of decent algae cultures, I am using bakers yeast to sustain the rotifer cultures. It keeps them alive, but they are not abundant enough or nutritious enough for the *P. fridmani* larvae. The stocks I have would be adequate for clownfish, however, since they would move quickly to brine shrimp napulii and would continue to take them as they mature. Although the *P. fridmani* larvae take brine shrimp very early, they do not continue to do so past day 10 to 13. I note that they often seem to pick copepods off the side of the glass tank, so I try to encourage the development of these benthic copepods in the rearing tanks.

The pair spawned again today, the second day after the last hatch. They are skipping a day between hatch and spawn on the last two spawns. Why? I have no idea. Perhaps the reproductive cycle is slowing down. They spawned in the late morning hours. Unlike clownfish, which almost always spawned in the late afternoon, *P. fridmani* apparently spawns at any time in the daylight hours, as soon as the male can convince the female to enter his nesting den.

March 26, 1996 2:30 PM

A note to the hatch of 3/23. I watched the hatching of the eggs at about 10:00 PM. The male had the egg ball in his hole in the rock, the hole was made by boring clams (all they do is sit there and pump water, very boring!) and it is about 4 inches deep and 1 1/4 inches in diameter. With a flashlight I was able to watch the tiny larval fish leave the hole. They flowed out over a very short period, 5 to 10 minutes. During hatching the male mouthed the egg ball, grabbed it in his mouth, worked it around, and moved it about the nest hole. He pushed water with his tail and pectoral fins toward the opening of the hole and flushed the larvae from the hole.

I believe that he also ate the remains of the egg ball after the larvae were hatched. I could see the egg ball before hatching, and the eyes of the larval fish within the eggs were a brilliant silver. After hatch, the egg ball was a uniform white in color without the sparkling eyes of the larvae. A bit later, the remains of the egg ball were not evident either in the nest or outside on the tank floor. He either ate the remains of the egg ball, or pushed it out of the hole where it was immediately taken by one of the cleaner shrimp in the aquarium. I'll watch more carefully on the next hatch, 3/29, and see if I can discern what happens to the exhausted egg ball. If he does eat it, then that may shed light on why he ate the eggs soon after they were laid for the first few spawns.

All the eggs hatch within 15 to 20 minutes after the first hatchlings appear. The male mouths and stimulates the eggs all during this procedure. I wonder if it is only the physical stimulation that the male provides that induces the eggs to hatch or if he also provides some type of chemical stimulation as well. I know that artificial stimulation of the eggs does not seem to provide the same degree of hatching. But at the time I was trying to hatch the eggs, I did not know that the male was so active with the egg ball at the time of hatch. I also wonder if the male provides the egg mass with some sort of protection from bacterial action. He does not appear to provide strong and continuous movement to the egg mass, which would provide oxygenation for the developing eggs, especially within the rather closed confines of the nesting hole. He does, however, wrap his body about the eggs frequently and even mouths them occasionally, behavior which could supply them with some substance that might control pathogenic bacterial growth. Something to follow up on someday.....

The newest larvae in tank C are doing well. I have cranked up the rotifers in that tank and thanks to the yeast feeding, I have sufficient rotifers. I enrich them with Selcon and algae for about 20 minutes before feeding and that does seem to help for at least the first 5 to 6 days.

The larvae in Tank C, including the oldest larvae moved over from B, are still surviving although the numbers are dropping. They are 14 days old at this point. The oldest larva, if he is still in there, is 19 days old. Geeze, at that age he should be getting color and becoming a juvenile. They do so well for the first 8 to 10 days. They should be easy to rear because of this.

The larvae in the 10 gallon tank are 9 days old and are dropping out rapidly. I just didn't have the rotifers to feed them properly during the first 3 to 6 days.

4

April 1996-

Larval Survival! Jubilation!

April 2, 1996, 4:30 PM

Wow, no entries for a whole week. I have let this journal slip. The spawn of 3/25 hatched on 3/29. I set up the video camera and used the big halogen flashlight to record the male hatching the eggs. The light did not seem to bother him much and I was able to get the entire procedure on video tape. He moved the eggs all around the den, grabbing them in his mouth and shaking the egg ball vigorously, then rolling the egg ball around his body and fanning it vigorously with his pectoral and tail fins. The eggs began to hatch and the tiny silvery larvae swarmed out of the mouth of the den. He kept up the agitation of the egg ball for about 20 minutes until all the larvae were hatched and there was nothing left of the egg ball.

I observed him occasionally snap up a larva, but he did not make a concerted effort to eat them. It is possible that without the light he would not have eaten any of them. He settled back into the den after the hatch and was no longer concerned about the fate of the larvae. I then siphoned up most of the larvae and ran them into larval tank C for a rearing run.

The pair spawned again the next day, 3/30 and the male held the eggs for a couple of days, but when I looked into the den today, the eggs were gone, evidently eaten by the male. This may have occurred because the male was disturbed during the last hatch, or because he was stimulated by the light to eat a few larvae during the last hatch. Whatever the cause, the spawn is lost, but they seem to be preparing to spawn again, and this will probably happen tomorrow since the female is showing a bit of rotundity today.

The larvae in all the other tanks have died out. This morning there were only 4 larvae surviving in tank B from the hatch of 3/23. I carefully scooped them from this tank and placed them in tank C. One thing I may do is to move the larvae to a new tank at about day 8, which will get the larvae away from the great accumulation of growing brine shrimp and allow, so to say, for a fresh start. They are not too hard to catch in a small cup, but you have to keep your eye on the them. It is very easy for them to disappear from sight just as you think you have them in the cup. They are very fast and very transparent, except for the eyes and the gut, so they can quickly disappear from view.

I moved the large 19 day old larva from tank B to tank C on about the 28th and then I observed him dead on the bottom a couple of days later. I thought for a while that this one would make it through, but no.

The hatch of 3/30 is now 4 days old and they seem to be doing very well. I tried some dry food, finely ground flake food, and they seemed interested but it was not possible to tell if they ate it or not from just "in tank" observation. I think I will continue to offer them this food once or twice a day in hopes that if they take it, it will provide some essential nutrients that they may be lacking.

Larvae from most previous spawns have died out at this point, only a few fish from the 3/23 hatch and the numerous larvae from the 3/29 hatch remain. All the cleaner shrimp larvae have died out as well. I saw the last larval shrimp on about the 28th. It was strong and feeding on brine shrimp and about 11 days old at that time.

I have given up on the algae cultures. The *T-isochrysis* is not coming up for me in the inside cultures. I think perhaps I have contaminated the cultures with ciliates and that may be why I am not getting good growth. I will try with the *Nanochloropsus* when I get it from Frank, to keep more pure cultures (Yes, I know, a culture is either pure or it isn't, one can't have degrees of pure, but I guess one can have degrees of contamination). Anyway, the outside culture is doing well, surprisingly enough. There are rotifers in the culture and the *T-isochrysis* is dark and in a good bloom. I am using yeast to keep the rotifer cultures going, a little bakers yeast in solution each day has the rotifers growing rapidly and abundantly. I don't know how nutritious they are, but at least I have enough to keep the rearing tanks full.

April 10, 1996

Busy times, I haven't kept up with the breeding or the journal very well in the last few days. The spawn that was to hatch on 4/3 was lost at about two days. I assume that the male ate the eggs, but this was not observed. The pair spawned again on 4/5 and this spawn hatched on 4/9. The pair did not spawn again today but it looks as if they will spawn tomorrow.

There are still a few, perhaps 6 to 10, larvae still alive from the hatch of 3/29. They are 12 days old today. I have been feeding them a particulate food twice a day, either

San Francisco brine shrimp larval diet, 80 to 250 microns, or a ground up very fine pellet food. I can't say for sure that they take this particulate food, but they do show great interest in the food clouds that descend from the surface. I have been a bit sparse in the feeding of brine shrimp napulii since I think that they may consume enough of this lipid rich food to damage their livers and that this may be the cause or at least contribute to the total mortalities that occur on day 12 to 16.

Julian was over last night and I gave him about half the hatch. He has placed this in a large coral culture system he has going, and we will see if any survive by feeding on the plankton that is present in this system. I also borrowed his plankton net, a good half meter, 53 micron net, with which I will get wild plankton to feed the hatches, and we will see if nutrition is the big stone wall I have been bumping up against. I will make the first plankton tows tomorrow.

April 11, 1996

All right... I used Julian's plankton net early this afternoon to collect copepods and other zooplankters for the two hatches that are still running. The plankton was collected at the foot of the 17 St. Causeway bridge, the west side. There is a concrete abutment that is close to the road and a place to park, not legal, but available, and this site is very close to the inlet so oceanic plankton is present during the incoming tide. I processed the plankton first through window screen, which is about 1000 microns, and then collected the plankton on top of a 53 micron mesh. This gives me a little too wide a range of plankton. I will have to find a 250 micron mesh to bring down the range to an acceptable level. There are some arrow worms (Chaetognaths) in the plankton that were not sifted out and this will cause a problem later. I'll have to treat the plankton with copper to knock them out before sorting for feeding. Two 15 minute tows provided more than enough plankton for three 8 gallon tanks.

The larvae are responding very well to the live plankton, swimming and feeding with great vigor. The plankton is also in a much wider size range than the rotifers and brine shrimp so this may be the answer. A few more days will tell.

The pair also spawned again today. She was quite heavy before the spawn so it should be a good sized egg ball this time. Now with the wild plankton available, I should be able to bring through a good number from this last hatch, at least I hope so.

April 15, 1996, 5:30 PM

I have been towing plankton, two 15 minute tows, every other day, a total of three collections so far. The plankton is taken from the west foot of the 17th Street bridge, which is very near the Port Everglades inlet. The plankton is good, a lot of copepods. I started feeding it to the larvae on the day of the last entry, 4/11. The oldest larvae in tank C were 13 days old when I started the plankton feeding. I observed them taking plankton and I had hoped that they would break past the 14 to 16 day barrier. This did not happen, they died out by day 15. If my theory is correct about the livers suffering fatty degeneration because of the heavy lipids in the brine shrimp, then this may make sense in that the livers were too far gone to allow survival.

The next hatch of *P. fridmani*, off on 4/9, were never fed much brine shrimp as the plankton tows began on 4/11. These larvae are 6 days old today and seem to be doing

well. They have been fed only rotifers and plankton, with
a very small amount of brine shrimp napulii, so far. They
have received plankton on 4/13, and today, 4/15. The numbers are less than they were at hatch, but the hatch was
small and was thinned by giving many to Julian, so there
weren't very many larvae at the beginning.

There will be a large hatch tonight and I have set up
tank C to receive it. This tank already has some plankton
from the tows today so it will have a small start.

There was a hatch of the golden cleaner shrimp on
4/13 and a hatch of the S. scutellatus on 4/14. These larvae
were placed in tank D and I will keep some plankton in
this tank to see if perhaps this will help them come
through.

April 20, 1996, 11:00 AM

Five days since the last entry, a terrible lapse, but then
we have been busy. Al and Judy spent a couple of days
with us and I finally finished reading and commenting on
Frank's book, that took a lot of time. Now I have two more
manuscripts to read. Between reading other people's
manuscripts and the breeding work, I don't have any time
to work on my own book.

Anyway, I am very encouraged, not euphoric, just encouraged on the development and survival of the last two
hatches of P. fridmani. There are 5, or at least 4, of the larvae
still surviving from the hatch of 4/9, the one I split with
Julian. The larvae are 11 days old today and there has been
no significant mortality for the last 3 or 4 days, although I
did notice one dead on the bottom this morning. They are
a bit larger than any other larvae have been at this age. Several are beginning to take up residence at one bottom corner of the tank, a good sign that their planktonic life is

nearing completion. There is not yet, however, any sign of coloration; the body is still quite transparent except for the gut and eyes. They are now about 6 or 7 mm long (1/4 inch or so) and they move all around the small tank with speed and ease. I do not expect coloration for another 5 days or so, but we shall see, I hope.

They feed on small zooplankton and rotifers. I get plankton every other day just before high tide, usually two 15 minute tows. The plankton is put in a 5 gallon bucket filled about three quarters full, transported to the van and placed in a large, 33 gallon, plastic tote box with a cover. The large surface area in the box keeps the plankton oxygenated during the trip home. When I am running only one or two tanks, I can keep half of the tow alive till the next day in a 5 gallon bucket with light aeration. There is a problem with chaetognaths and medusa getting through the straining mesh (I still don't have the 105, 250, and 500 micron mesh material to make good plankton sieves; however, I did get some kitchen sieves at the Publix supermarket that are about 500 and 800 microns and these are a great improvement over several layers of 1000 micron window screening.)

The chaetognaths are very efficient planktonic predators. I saw one this morning feeding on a slightly smaller chaetognath. It ate it like a snake eating a huge rat. I thought they would both die, but the bigger one just crammed the smaller one down and looked for more. I know that they can eat fish larvae if they can catch them and if they don't succeed in catching and eating them, just the encounter is enough to kill the larvae. Perhaps that is what happened to the larvae I saw dead this morning. I used the 500 micron sieve to remove many of the chaetognaths this morning. It was possible to do this because the larvae were so few that I could sweep the strainer through the tank for the chaetognaths and avoid catching the fish larvae.

This hatch has been fed very little brine shrimp so far. The presence of the larger plankton has substituted nicely for the brine shrimp napulii and I think that this has enabled the larvae to get this far along. I have siphoned the detritus from the bottom of the tank twice so far, which also results in a partial water change, and I plan to do this again late this PM. I discovered another feeding method that may be very important. I can take a ball of frozen, peeled shrimp and, while it is still very frozen, rub it gently on a fine grater over a bowl of cold water. The tiny particles land in the water and maintain their form as discrete particles without clumping together. Then by passing the water though a 500 micron screen, the small particles are separated from the larger particles. These very tiny particles range from the size of rotifers to the size of large brine shrimp napulii. The are also so small that they remain suspended in the water column for some time and the larvae can feed upon them. I have not used this feeding method much in the last few days because I have sufficient wild plankton, but I plan to experiment with this method at a later date and see if I can rear the larvae with only rotifers and shrimp particles. The use of the shrimp particles will require that the tank bottoms be siphoned at least every two days.

Another recent discovery is that I can use a 10x lens, one typically used to examine 35 mm slides, to find out what the larvae are feeding on and get an idea of what types and densities of larval food organisms are in the rearing tanks. Holding the lens to the side of the tank provides a good view of the tiniest copepod napulii, rotifers, and even particles of dead food that pass by the focal point of the lens. The depth of field of the lens is only about 5 mm, but the lens can be moved in and out quickly and a particular particle can be followed long enough to identify it easily. A lens that can be removed from its base is best, such as the TASCO lens, since this provides a good range of movement from the inside glass surface to almost 4 cm (1 1/2 inches) within the tank. I have even been able to follow individual fish larvae long enough to observe the food items in the gut and even to watch the coil, strike, and ingestion of specific food items. One can also see enough "tank space" to get an idea of the type and amount of food organisms that are in the tank.

I no longer have a decent algal base for rotifer rearing and enrichment. Frank is reestablishing his cultures and I hope he will send some *Nannochloropsus* soon. I am using yeast and Frank's "RotiRich", which has some Spirulina in it, to keep the rotifers going. This works all right, but the cultures become organic laden very quickly and have to be reestablished (more work) every few days. I am also enriching the rotifers with "Super Selco" now rather than "Selcon", which may be more beneficial to the larval fish.

The *P. fridmani* hatch of 4/15 is now 5 days old and they are very numerous in the tank. I added the remaining plankton from yesterday's tows to the tank this AM and, unfortunately, there were some chaetognaths in this batch. The chaetognaths are present in the high tide plankton, but not so much in the low tide tows. But the high tide tows produce better and more abundant copepod napulii, and the chaetognaths, at least the large ones, can be removed by sieving through a 500 micron mesh. I forgot to pass the tow saved from yesterday through the 500 micron strainer, which would have removed most of them. It is not possible to pull them out of this tank with the strainer since there are so many small fish larvae. I have to keep my fingers crossed and hope that I don't lose too many larvae in this run to the evil and predacious chaetognaths. I did see the remains of one fish larvae in the digestive system of a small medusa that is also on the loose in this tank. Like I need another problem to deal with. The fish larvae are feeding well, however, and are good size for 5 days. This is the first numerous hatch that I have been able to feed wild plankton and Super Selco rotifers from the very beginning. It will be interesting to see how it progresses.

There is another *P. fridmani* spawn in the process of incubation right now, spawned on 4/17 and should hatch on 4/21. I will prepare Tank D for them today. The shrimp larvae died out only a few days after the last hatch. I don't know what happened since I did not follow them closely. It is difficult with limited facilities and limited time to follow more than one experimental rearing project at a time.

April 22, 1996, 11:00 PM

My hopes are rising for bringing through a few *P. fridmani* from the hatch of 4/9. There are four late larval fish in Tank B from this hatch, 13 days old today. I found one dead in this tank yesterday and it had orchid chromatophores forming on the lower jaw and along the body. Metamorphosis can't be far away. They are now spending most of their time in the corners of the tank and along the sides. I gave this tank a partial water change on 4/20 and siphoned the bottom. Wild plankton is still the main food although I have also given them a little new hatch brine shrimp, just a small amount on the 20th and again today, and some enriched rotifers mixed with the plankton feeding. There are still a number of chaetognaths in this tank, but the larval fish are now too big to be taken by them, or so I hope.

The larvae, from the hatch of 4/15, in Tank C are 7 days old today. They are still quite numerous and are growing very well. If they do as well as the 4/9 hatch, I would expect to get quite a few through. I have seen larvae taken by both chaetognaths and medusa, however, I can only hope that the predation will not be too great. I can probably selectively remove chaetognaths and medusa with a 3/8 inch siphon by bringing the end of the siphon close to the predator and then quickly opening the outside end of the siphon to created a rapid, but brief, suction. Undoubtedly I would also remove some larval fish by this method and if they were not recoverable, the loss might be greater than that to predation. The larvae in this tank have been fed wild plankton, the fraction between 53 and 500 microns, which includes a fraction that is a bit too large, and enriched rotifers. No brine shrimp napulii have been fed. Mortality is low and the larvae look strong and large for day 7.

The male ate the spawn of 4/17, so there was no hatch on 4/21. They will spawn again today or tomorrow, so there should be another hatch to work within about 5 or 6 days.

I have been keeping about half of the plankton for 24 hours in an aerated 5 gallon bucket. This seems to work well as it preserves most of the zooplankton alive for feeding the next day. This gives the larvae a new plankton feed each day instead of every other day. If I get the plankton on the full flow of the high tide there is enough in two 15 minute tows with the half meter, 53 micron net to amply feed at least two 10 gallon tanks for two days.

At this point, it sure looks like nutritional factors have been the major cause of failure in the runs previous to the use of wild plankton. I suspect that the problem was the use of brine shrimp napulii and I think that the accumulation of heavy lipids in the larval fish (or perhaps a toxic problem with the specific can of eggs I have been using?) is the cause of the mortality rather than a lack of a specific nutritional factor, although that could also be the problem. I will try some non wild plankton runs using Super Selco enriched rotifers and tiny particles of raw shrimp when I get a good *Nanochloropsus* based culture system going.

I have not had much success with the two species of *Stenopus* cleaning shrimp that I have worked with so far, but I have not put a lot of effort into rearing them. I now have *Lysmata debelius* with eggs and *Lysmata amboinensis* with eggs and these should hatch in a week or sooner perhaps. It will be interesting to see what I can do with these species with a wild plankton source.

April 23, 1996, 4:00 PM

There are still 3 late larvae in Tank B that are 14 days old today. They look good, swimming all over the tank, around and in-between the chaetognaths, feeding on zooplankton, and seemingly, a bit on rotifers. They are about 1/2 inch long, a little over a cm, and look like little fish except that they have no observable orchid pigment at this point.

The larvae in Tank C are 8 days old today and are about 5 mm long. They are actively swimming about the tank feeding on zooplankton and rotifers. There are many, many chaetognaths in the tank with these larvae and I am sure that the chaetognaths are feeding on the larvae, especially at night. I looked with a flashlight last night and saw a number of chaetognaths with dark guts, a good, no a bad, sign that they are feeding on the larvae. The larvae are still numerous, though, perhaps as many as 100 remain, which is very good for day 8. I can only hope that the larvae will outgrow the chaetognaths prey range before they are all gone.

The scarlet cleaner shrimp, *Lysmata debelius*, spawned last night, 4/22. The larvae are small and red, although they seemed larger than the *Stenopus* larvae. I have set these up in larval Tank D and have fed them rotifers and the smallest fraction of the wild plankton today. So far mortality has been slight and they number about 100, which is a guess. There were more, but not all could be captured from the adult breeding tank. They were very positively phototropic and gathered densely in the beam of a small flashlight.

It is difficult getting them out of the brood stock tank. I have an acrylic cover over the tank to keep down evaporation and salt creep and I balance the flashlight on the top of the cover in the corner so that the light beam runs down the corner of the tank and the larvae gather up into the beam. The 3/8 inch siphon then goes into the 2 inch feeding hole in the acrylic cover and I can move the end of the siphon up and down the beam, collect the larvae, and then deposit them in the larval rearing tank just below the brood tank. However if one is not careful, then the upper part of the siphon can knock against the flashlight, causing it to fall over, and then the flashlight, in a move that one could not duplicate no matter how hard one tried, can fall precisely into the feeding hole and drift slowly to the bottom of the tank, which considerably interrupts the entire larval capture process.

Interestingly, the larvae seem to lose some of their intense phototropism within an hour or so after hatch. I also noticed this with the *P. fridmani*, but not as pronounced as with the *L. debelius*. I will make a good try with the scarlet shrimp, using plankton and rotifers, steering away from the brine shrimp napulii as much as possible, and see how they progress.

5:30 PM

The Dottybacks spawned again. They went off I think, about 2 or 3 PM since I saw them courting about 1 and now at 5:30 there is a nest of eggs in the male's den and the female suddenly looks a lot slimmer. If the male holds this egg ball without eating it, then it should hatch on Sat. night, 4/27.

April 24, 1996, 12:10 PM

There are still 3 late larval orchid dottybacks in the Tank B. They still look good and are feeding well now at day 15. I added some day old wild plankton and the enriched rotifers, as usual.

There has been considerable mortality in the dottybacks in Tank C over the last two days. There are still numerous larvae in this tank at day 9, perhaps about 50, (which is much, much better then any pre wild plankton runs) but they are not nearly as numerous as they were a couple of days ago. I suspect that the chaetognaths have taken quite a few, but there has also been some losses due to lack of feeding? or other causes. I siphoned the bottom yesterday and there were quite a few dead larvae on the bottom of the bucket. The larvae remaining, however, look quite good and vigorous. I fed them day old wild plankton and enriched rotifers this morning. I also enriched the wild plankton for about 2 hours this morning with Frank's

RotiRich. I did feed this tank, and Tank B, yesterday PM with a little bit of new hatch brine shrimp napulii, which may have contributed to the mortality in Tank C, if there is a problem with the brine shrimp napulii, but I doubt that a small supplemental feeding of brine shrimp napulii would have such a rapid and lethal effect.

The *L. debelius* larvae are all present and seem to be doing well at day 2. They are hanging in the water column and seem to be feeding well. There is a tendency to gather in one corner of the tank, but that corner is also where the plankton accumulates and apparently it is sort of "lunch counter" for the *L. debelius* larvae.

The male is still watching over his rather large egg ball, now about a day old. If he continues to incubate the eggs, there should be a large hatch on Saturday night, 4/27. It doesn't look as if there will be a larval tank free by that time, so I will probably get the auxiliary 10 gallon tank set up for it.

April 25, 1996, 10:00 AM

Damn Chaetognaths! There has been increased mortality in Tank C, the larvae are 10 days old today, hatch of

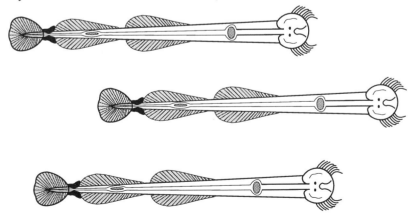

Chaetognaths or Arrow Worms, genus *Sagitta* (also known as Damnchaetognaths).

4/15, and they are looking good. Size is increasing and
their mobility is all over the small tank. The chaetognaths
have also grown up, however, and they are quite numerous, at least 50. Many had dark guts this morning and the
numbers of larvae have diminished. I siphoned the bottom
of the tank and there were only one or two dead larvae in
the detritus. I know the chaetognaths are chowing down
on the larvae. In the light, the larvae seem to be able to
avoid the chaetognaths, but in the dark the larvae drift
about and the chaetognaths are able to encounter them
more easily (quite a deadly encounter group for the larvae).

I can eliminate the chaetognaths from the plankton by
treating it with about 0.2 or 0.3 ppm copper during the half
hour transport back to the fish room, or limit them significantly by filtering the plankton for the smallest larvae
through a very fine, about 200 micron, mesh. Sieving
through the fine mesh removes the adult chaetognaths and
all but the smallest juveniles and eggs. This way the chaetognaths are too small to prey on the larvae and the larvae
have a good chance to outgrow the chaetognaths. I would
go with the copper in a large scale operation, but for now I
think I will try the sieving, even though I don't yet have a
mesh smaller than about 400. I'm afraid if I treat the plankton with copper, I may introduce copper levels into the
very small larval tanks and also the copper would not be
compatible with the *Lysmata debelius* larvae that I am also
trying to rear. The larvae in Tank C are still numerous
enough so that I think I'll get at least a half dozen though
and I'll be more careful with the plankton and sieve it as
fine as I can with the next hatch.

I gave both Tank B and C a water change and a bottom
siphon this AM, and Tank C also got a small dose of streptomycin as well. I also added a small dose of streptomycin

to Tank D as well. The *L. debelius* larvae are still doing well, day 3, I noted a molt floating by when I examined the tank with the 10 X lens, I also noted what appeared to be a stunted larva ? so I also added a few drops of an iodine supplement to help molting. All the tanks were fed enriched rotifers and a little brine shrimp napulii. I will get plankton early afternoon, the tides are not right until about noontime, so the plankton feeding will be a bit late today.

April 26, 1996, 11:20 AM

The plankton was a bit late yesterday, high tide wasn't till 2:30 and although I towed at about 1 PM, I still didn't get the plankton into the tank till about 3 PM. The dottybacks are doing fine, however, the 3 in Tank B, day 17 today, are now about 3/4 inch in length (about 15 mm) and look like they will get their color any day now. This will be the big breakthrough. When they pick up the adult color, it will be the jump from larval to juvenile stage. The larval *P. fridmani* in Tank C are also doing well, there are still too many to count, somewhere between 30 and 50, and they seem to be too large now for the chaetognaths to grasp, about 5 to 7 mm. They are at day 11 today. I fed the rest of the wild plankton this AM and I will feed some enriched rotifers later today, and perhaps also a few brine shrimp napulii.

Disaster in the *Lysmata debelius* tank! It is now day 4 for them and they seemed to be doing very well yesterday. They were numerous, had good color, and were very active. I observed them through the 10 X lens and they were swimming strongly and appeared to be feeding, however, despite an hour or so of observation, I did not actually observe a larvae taking or feeding on a food organism. This morning there were only a few remaining alive. The survivors seemed more listless and were obviously not feeding. Mortality seemed to be at least 80 to 90 percent. The reason for this mortality is not at all clear. A few possibilities:

- 1. Environmental problems. A problem with the first molt. Perhaps there was a lack of iodine or some other element that prevented a successful first molt. They did very well for the first three days with little or no mortality and strong activity so I doubt that there was anything fundamentally wrong with the environment, such as lighting, salinity, temperature, etc. that would prevent survival. There was some natural sea water introduced with the plankton so I doubt that a total lack of iodine or any other trace element was the problem.

- 2. Toxins. I did treat this tank, Tank D, with a small dose of streptomycin yesterday and it is possible that this is toxic to *L. debelius*, although I seriously doubt that this is the problem. However, in the next rearing run I will not treat with antibiotics. It could well be that a bacterial toxin (a form of Toxic Tank Syndrome) is responsible. This is usually the case when almost total mortality occurs in a tank that has been doing well right up to the time that the mortality occurs.

- 3. Starvation. It is possible that despite the wild plankton, rotifers, and brine shrimp, there was not enough of the specific food organisms that they require, or not enough food organisms of the right size or type to provide proper nutrition. Next run I will feed more heavily with enriched rotifers, which will at least increase the number of small food organisms available to the larval shrimp. I did feed the survivors a greater amount of rotifers this morning, along with the remains of the wild plankton, so perhaps this will help the survivors. I strongly suspect that the problem lies in the realm of nutrition and I will work on this aspect first.

(I'm not sure that I will get back to *Lysmata* culture anytime soon, so I will add an excerpt here from the *Lysmata* journal on the results of later work with *Lysmata debelius*. I ran several rearing attempts with this species of shrimp. I was not successful in bringing them through the larval stage, but there is one entry that sort of tells the story. I will slip it in here just to tie up this loose end a little bit better at this time.

January 5, 1997, 2:00 PM

Day 14, 2:00 PM. Well, all the *Lysmata debelius* larvae in the VRT (vertical rearing tank) died out yesterday. They went very suddenly, overnight. Yet the larvae in the mint container are still alive today, zero mortality. Same hatch, same food, same age, same water, same light, only different containers, and suddenly, after 13 days of culture, only one of the containers experiences total mortality, and this is the same type of total mortality that hit most of the previous runs, although usually earlier in the run... Hmmm... This makes sense only if the mortality was caused by a bacterial toxin. Any other cause would be either gradual or would include both rearing environments.

My opinion at this point is that the cause of the total mortality of larval *Lysmata* shrimp that usually occurs some time in the first 15 days of development is caused by an environmental factor that develops within the rearing tank. I suspect some type of bacterial toxin, even though I used an antibiotic, streptomycin, during most of expermen-

tal *Lysmata* rearing runs. Most other "natural" causes of
mortality occur more gradually, a loss of larvae over several days or a week rather than an almost instantous, total
mortality. This species has been reared at several hatcheries, although not in large numbers, on apparently just rotifers and brine shrimp. The larval stage apparently extends
to about 40 days. The length of the larval stage in captive
culture depends, I'm sure, on the water quality and nutritional regime that are presented to the larvae. The larval
stage may be as short as 30 days or as long as 60 days.
Some aquarists have kept the larvae as long as 65 days
without metamorphosis into juveniles. A careful and dedicated hobbyist has a chance to rear *Lysmata* sp. but I think
that there will be a steep learning curve.)

April 27, 1996, 11:30 AM

Damn chaetognaths! I am going to have to treat the
plankton with copper for future fish runs. The chaetognaths are unacceptably reducing the larval population in
Tank C. Through the magnifying glass, I can see good
sized *P. fridmani* larvae stuffed into the transparent
guts of those mindless predators. And it figures, if one chaetognath can eat another
chaetognath that is the same size
as it, there is no reason
why it can't scarf
down a fish lar-
vae that is no
more than
half its size.
Now there are more chaetognaths than fish in that tank. I
still have about 20 fish larvae, however, and now at day 12,
most of them look good so I am hoping for at least 6 to

come through on this run. Geeze, these are going to be expensive little fish!

I experimented with feeding small particulate raw shrimp bits this morning. I lightly grated frozen shrimp over the tiny grater into cold fresh water. Then I passed the grated shrimp through a 1000 micron mesh (window screen) and then through a strainer with about a 400 or 500 micron mesh. The shrimp particles that made it through the last mesh were quite small, about like brine shrimp napulii and even smaller, and since they were infused with fresh water, they floated and swirled in the tank currents for several minutes. I observed both the oldest larvae, Tank B, now 18 days old and the 12 day old larvae apparently feeding on them. This may work in the stead, or as a supplement, to brine shrimp napulii, but it will take a lot of time to prepare and feed the shrimp particles. Also as an only or even main food, it will have to be fed three or four times a day and the tank bottom siphoned at least once a day. The shrimp particles can be stored in the refrigerator in a jar of cold water for two or three days and this may help reduce the time requirement. I then fed each tank enriched rotifers and I will also feed wild plankton that I get this afternoon.

There is a new hatch of *P. fridmani* due off this evening and I will put some in Tank D where the *Lysmata* shrimp were (there are still a few left) and also set up the 10 gallon tank for this next run.

April 28, 1996, 12:30 PM

The *P. fridmani* hatch came off last night as scheduled, a good size hatch, probably at least 800 larvae. I set up the 10 gallon tank and siphoned most into it, and since there were only a very few *Lysmata debelius* shrimp still in Tank

D, I siphoned a number of larvae into it as well, which seemed like a good move since this tank already had a good population of plankton that would otherwise go to waste. I made a small goof while siphoning and also got a few larvae into Tank C, unfortunately more food for the chaetognaths. I doubt that any of the larvae accidentally introduced in Tank C will make it. I will watch the food levels in both the new tanks and try to keep the larger plankton down to manageable levels. I also have the *Nanochloropsus* algae coming up now and I can add some of this to the rearing tanks. This should also be helpful.

The three late larvae in Tank B are now 19 days old and still doing very well. They seem to be almost an inch long now. Still no adult coloration. The guts are white or pink, depending on the food organisms and the rest of the body is transparent with a little dark pigmentation showing up now. The larvae in Tank C are now 13 days old and they do seem a bit too large for the chaetognaths now. There are only about 10 or 12 larvae left as near as I can tell.

I started the *Nanochloropsus* cultures last Tuesday, 4/23, I now have 4 gallons of culture, 2 strong and 2 just started. I am enriching the rotifers with Super Selco and *Nanochloropsus* for about 4 to 6 hours before feeding to the larvae. I can keep the rotifer cultures producing by using yeast and Frank's RotiRich, a yeast, vitamin, and spirulina media. The cultures need changing often but they do keep me in rotifers. The rotifer demand has lessened somewhat since I have also started using wild plankton.

There is a problem with the wild plankton, however, besides those damn chaetognaths. It is hard to get enough of the smallest fraction, that under about 180 to 200 microns in the rearing tanks. I think that may be what caused the wipe out of the *Lysmata* larvae. Although there were a

"Low Tech" algae culture in glass gallon jars. The plastic tops of the jars have a small hole that permits entry of a section of rigid air tubing. Air bubbles up from the tube opening at the bottom of the jar and keeps the algae aerated and suspended.

lot of "food organisms" in the tank, most were larger than 200 microns and there may not have been enough in the size range required by the new larvae. I will order a range of micron sized nylon mesh tomorrow so that I can better size the plankton to the needs of the particular larvae.

April 30, 1996, 2:30 PM

Today was not a good day to get plankton. Low tide was at 12:30 PM, which means that to get plankton somewhere near high tide, I would have to catch the outgoing tide at 9 AM or earlier, or incoming tide at 4 PM or later. I chose the early time to make sure that the larvae had food during the day since I had had a real good collection on

Saturday, and had enough left over plankton to skip collection on Monday.

Of course I got there a little late, about 9:30 AM and the tide was already a bit too low for a good towing current, and just as I got there it started to pour, and a drainage pipe from the road is located right at the best plankton collection site and it was pouring road runoff into the water, and the wind was blowing about 30 mph in the opposite direction of the current, which piled up a rather high swell, and after driving 20 miles to get the plankton, I wasn't about to go home empty-handed. I waited till the rain stopped, almost, and did get some plankton by repeatedly dipping the net and pulling it up to manually strain as much water as my back would let me. Needless to say, the plankton today was not rich, but because my rearing tanks are so small, it was adequate.

The rotifers are now up very strong in the outside 30 gallon tank. There is not much algae in the tank, but I feed it the yeast based RotiRich every day and the rotifer population remains adequate. The salinity is high, about 40, because I have been adding waste plankton water to it once in a while, also some tap water to keep the salinity from really going off the scale. I will have to pull this tank down half way sometime soon and exchange the 50% with new saltwater. The rotifers are enriched with algae

The rotifer, with eggs.

and Super Selco for several hours before feeding. This maintains a base of nutritious small food organisms in the rearing tanks which I supplement with the wild plankton, some days more than others, and a little brine shrimp napulii.

The three largest *P. fridmani* are still doing well at day 21. They appear to be about 20 mm long, a bit over 3/4 inch and behave like small fish rather than larvae. There is still no observable orchid coloration. The body is still transparent with a little bit of dark pigment. The dark pigment is located in the center of the side of the body and appears to be gradually increasing.

There are 8 (as near as I can count) 14 day old larvae remaining from the hatch of 4/15. They are sharing the tank with the damn chaetognaths and seem to be large enough (and smart enough) to avoid these predators. I gave both Tanks B and C a water change yesterday. The 8 larvae are now about 8 to 10 mm long and move actively about the tank feeding on the larger plankton.

The 3 day old larvae from the hatch of 4/27 are set up in Tank D and in the 10 gallon tank. So far there has been very little mortality and the larvae are feeding very well. I am sure much of the mortality in the last run (Tank C) was due to assuming that there was abundant food in the tank because the larger zooplankton were so abundant, but actually there was very little of the smaller food organisms of the size required by the tiny larvae. This time I am using more of the rotifers to maintain the abundance of the tiny food organisms. Taking a sample of water directly from the tank and examining it under the dissecting microscope and viewing the food organisms in the tank with the 10 X lens are good ways of evaluating the abundance of the smaller organisms.

There was a hatch last night of the golden coral cleaner shrimp *Stenopus* sp. and *Stenopus scutellatus*. I had no tanks that were not occupied with larvae and had to let both spawns, for the most part, pass. I did siphon out a few of the golden cleaners into Tank D and the 10 gallon tank. I had to add a few to these tanks just to see how they do, even if they only last for a few days.

The *P. fridmani* pair spawned again yesterday, 4/29. This means that if the male doesn't eat the eggs, which he has been doing lately on every other hatch, they will hatch on Friday, 5/3. I don't have an empty tank now that some of the larvae are making it through the larval stage, almost. I may move the remaining larvae out of Tank C and into the 10 gallon tank, there are only a few in Tank C anyway, and I do have one from that hatch in that tank already. I was trying to catch out some of the chaetognaths and caught up one of the larval fish in the process. It still seemed viable so I put it into the 10 gallon tank and it has survived so far among all the smaller 3 day old larvae.

This marine fish rearing is a very time consuming business. Actually, it's not a business because I could never get $5,000.00 each for the fish. I don't think anyone with a full time job could ever rear these things, even just experimentally. Clownfish, yes, they are much less demanding of time and attention. But then, on the other hand, once a routine system for rearing the dottybacks is developed, when one knows exactly what is required and when, then it may not be quite as consuming of time and effort to rear them.

5

May 1996 -

A Flash of Purple

May 1, 1996, 10:30 AM

In Tank C, on the bottom, in the corner, partially hidden from casual inspection, a patch of HYDROIDS! These Cnidaria, class Hydrozoa, come in with the wild plankton as small medusa and establish a colony on the sides or bottom of the tank. They are quite "sticky" and have to be scraped off from their attachment. The colony is composed of dense growths of tiny polyps that form whitish to greenish patches, depending on how much filamentous algae is entwined within the patch. The polyps have tiny tentacles with potent stinging cells and they feed on anything that drifts into their reach. The patches develop an orange hue from feeding on brine shrimp or whitish from feeding on rotifers or copepods. Any larval fish that happen to drift into their grasp are quickly killed and held by the polyps.

I found two of the eight, 15 day old *P. fridmani* larvae dead in this hydroid patch this morning. Evidently they drifted into the patch at night and were killed. The patch is now gone, I scraped it up and siphoned it out, but this is another hazard of wild plankton, which, in most instances, can be eliminated or greatly reduced by treating the plankton briefly (only during transportation) with .2 ppm copper. I will move the remaining 4 or 5 larvae today into the 10 gallon tank and clean up Tank C for the hatch on Friday.

I think I can see the very beginnings of coloration on the now 22 day old late larvae in Tank B. The head of the largest of the three has a slight orange tinge and the body does not seem quite as transparent as the other two larvae.

The 4 day old larvae are looking good. They are feeding very well, mostly on the enriched rotifers since the last plankton collection was so sparse. I will go tomorrow very early to catch the incoming tide at 7 AM and with luck, I'll get a good collection for two or three days of feeding. The ten gallon tank was filled with a combination of natural sea water and artificial sea water and treated with about 800 mg of streptomycin sulfate. I have siphoned the bottom only once so far.

2:20 PM

I moved the 4 remaining *P. fridmani* larvae in Tank C to the 10 gallon tank. There are many large chaetognaths in Tank C now despite frequent attempts to net them from the tank. I will clean this tank up for the hatch on Friday. There are many 4 day old larvae in the 10 gallon tank and now also five 15 day old larvae. They all seem to be feeding and growing well, there are also a few *Stenops sp.* larvae in this tank.

Strangely, I can find no larval *P. fridmani* in Tank D. This was the tank in which all the *Lysmata debelius* died out in only 3 days. I also can't find any *Stenopus* larvae in that tank either. There is plenty of plankton, and a number of chaetognaths in that tank as well, but not enough to have taken all the larvae that were put in that tank. I don't know what happened in that tank. I may clean it up completely for the Friday hatch and try a few in there just to see what happens.

May 2, 1996, 2:20 PM

Good plankton this morning. Not great, but quite good. I hit the top of the incoming tide at 7:30 AM and even though there was a lot of oil and flotsam in the water, the net rode just below the surface on a gentle current and the catch was good. Mostly small stuff, zooplankters under 250 microns. The micron netting I ordered came in yesterday, 150 and 250 microns, and I made up two sieves, one at each size. Plastic peanut butter jars (the chunky kind) make excellent sieves. Cut out most of the top, leaving only about a half inch of the top around the rim, and cut the bottom off the jar. Place a section of the nylon mesh over the top of the jar and screw the cut out top on quite

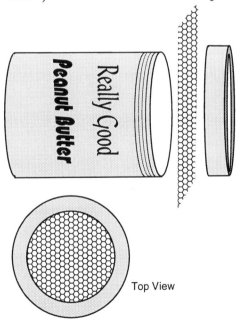

Top View

A plankton/rotifer sieve made out of a plastic food container with the bottom cut off and nylon mesh screen placed between the cut out top and the container body.

tight. Trim off the excess mesh cloth. The result is a sieve that holds about a pint and concentrates plankton and rotifers quite nicely.

Almost everything today went through the 250 micron sieve. I don't know why everything collected was so small, perhaps because of the sluggish current or perhaps because of the early morning time, or the season of the year. Who knows?

I placed a small rock in Tank B yesterday because I thought that the 23 day old (today) *P. fridmani* larvae looked like they were ready to move into bottom habitat and I wanted to have something available. This morning I could not find one of the three larvae. I was worried and moved the rock and there he was hiding under the rock and not swimming in the water column as were the other two. He (sexually presumptuous, aren't I) is darker than the other two, which are still transparent except for the gut and eyes, but I still don't see the brilliant orchid adult coloration.

The other larvae, five 16 day old and a large number of 5 day old fish, are doing well in the 10 gallon tank. There has evidently been some mortality of the younger larval fish in this tank overnight. This is the time, 4 to 7 days, when there is a considerable drop in numbers. Plankton was also poor over the last couple of days and this may have contributed to the mortality, even though I did keep good levels of enriched rotifers in the tank. I am also adding a little *Nanochloropsus* algae to the rearing tank each day.

May 3, 1996, 5:30 PM

Tired. Busy day. The *P. fridmani* are doing fine. The male kept his egg ball and they should hatch tonight. I cleaned up larval Tanks C and D for this hatch. There was a pot load of DCs (damn chaetoghanths) in Tank C. There must have been at least 200. I think they have been reproducing in that tank. There's probably some graduate student somewhere wailing in frustration because he can't raise chaetognaths. It's easy, first spawn some expensive marine tropical fish...

I'm keeping a greater concentration of enriched rotifers in the 10 gallon tank for this run and there seems to be less mortality in the 6 day old larvae. There are a great many of them and they are now moving rapidly all about the tank. The three 24 day old larvae are still doing fine and growing well. One is residing under the rock and the other two are still in the corner, sort of in the water column, and none has yet taken on the orchid coloration of the adults.

May 5, 1996, 12:05 PM
Hallelujah! I picked up the rock in Tank B this morning and there was flash of bright orchid purple swimming around the rock! The three oldest P. fridmani are 26 days old today. I think the largest of the larvae metamorphosed completely yesterday but I didn't check him out yesterday since Winston, my 7 year old grandson, was over for the day and we had to go on a bird watch hike. But anyway, now I know that it takes about 23 to 28 days for P. fridmani to go through the larval stage. The other two appear to be picking up some color and they are just as large as the juvenile under the rock, but they are still wandering the small tank and have not yet become truly benthic. I would expect that they will also metamorphose in a few days.

The larvae in the 10 gallon tank are mixed spawns, the 5 oldest are 19 days today and the youngest are 8 days old today. The 19 day old larvae are about 10 mm (all sizes estimated by observation through the tank side, of course) and the 8 day old larvae are about 5 mm. They all seem to be doing quite well, the 8 day old larvae are still very numerous, perhaps a 100 or so. The cleaner shrimp larvae seem to be gone, at least I did not observe any in the tank today. I will have to concentrate on them only, especially in the area of foods and feeding, before I will have a chance to bring them through.

The *P. fridmani* spawn of 4/29 hatched on schedule the evening of 5/3. Interestingly, the entire egg ball did not hatch. There was about a third of the eggs that did not develop. The rest hatched normally and the larvae, now 2 days old are feeding normally. I don't know if the eggs were not totally fertilized or if some of the eggs died in early development. I noticed during hatching that many of the eggs did not have the bright eye spots that are visible in the eggs under the light of the flashlight. At the end of the hatch, the male pushed the remaining eggs out of the den and the golden cleaner shrimp immediately grabbed the dead eggs and began feeding on them. The pair of *P. fridmani* spawned again on 5/4 and the eggs look good as of right now. Well, we shall see how it goes.

May 6, 1996, 5:30 PM

Alas, the learning curve is steep. I lost one of the 3 oldest, 27 days, *P. fridmani* today. I couldn't find but 2 in the tank this morning, one completely metamorphosed into the juvenile form and one just beginning the transformation. I thought that the middle one must be deep in the rock going through the change. Then, about 20 minutes ago, I found a tiny, all purple, *P. fridmani* dried up on the floor of the fish room. Evidently, the second one metamorphosed and the oldest juvenile elected not to share the tank with the newcomer and chased him till he jumped from the tank, a leap of at least 1.5 inches over the side of the tank. I will have to provide a lot of cover for the metamorphosing juveniles and keep a cover on the tank. The third larvae is now in the process of metamorphosing and I did put a cover on the tank and added a few pieces of PVC pipe. I saw the changeling within a PVC coupling and I hope that they will survive together.

The male also ate the eggs this time, or at any rate, the egg ball is no longer in the den and is nowhere to be seen. It may be that I need to feed the male a bit better, especially when he is brooding. I feed shaved shrimp about two to three times a week, it should be at least one feeding a day. This may cut down on the loss of eggs. I have, however, run out places to put the new larvae. I was thinking of setting up another 20 gallon larval tank on a table in my office. This is dangerous, I don't have the time or space to start fooling around with mass production again. But then, it's only one more tank.

The larvae in the 10 gallon tank are doing fine. The 20 day old larvae still number 5 and they are picking up some orchid coloration, at least I can see this tint when I look down on the them. The 9 day old larvae are still very numerous, I bet there are at least 75, maybe 100 in the tank. They are feeding on rotifers, wild plankton and just a smidgen of brine shrimp napulii.

The hatch of 5/3 is 3 days old today. They are set up in Tanks C and D. I have been feeding tank C, which has by far the most larvae, wild plankton and rotifers, and Tank D, with only a few larvae, only rotifers. I am interested in the developmental differences that may occur. I will, if time allows, try to get Tank D through without wild plankton, or at least see how long they can survive.

May 9, 1996, 11:00 AM

OK, so I've been too busy to write down what's happening during the last three days. Well, that's life. I added a pile of little rocks in Tank B so that the new juvenile would have a place of his own. He didn't take to the PVC couplings, too sparse, I guess, but he did immediately jump into the rock pile. Now there is one fist sized rock and a small pile of rocks and each has a juvenile *P. fridmani* in occupancy. These juveniles are now 30 days old.

There are still 5 late stage larvae from the hatch of 4/15 that are 23 days old today. They seem to be picking up their orchid color. It is easier to see the color on these larvae since I can view them from the top and not just from the side. They are in the 10 gallon tank along with the 12 day old larvae from the spawn of 4/27. I will soon put little pyramids made from PVC pipe into this tank to give the new juveniles some habitat. I'm sure there are over 50 of the 12 day old larvae in this tank and they all look very good at this point. I am keeping some enriched rotifers in the tank and feeding wild plankton. I still collect the wild plankton, two 15 minute tows each in a volume of about 4 gallons, every other day. I feed half on the day of collection and half I keep under aeration, with a little bit of algae added, and then feed it the next day. I have made a water change of about 25% twice in the 10 gallon tank. I siphon the bottom as a part of each change and then let the water sit for about 30 minutes and then decant it though a 53 micron sieve to recover the food organisms. I then add a small amount of streptomycin to the tank, about 100 mg (50 mg per gallon of the new water).

The latest spawn is 6 days old today, they are in two tanks, C and D. Tank C gets enriched rotifers and wild plankton and Tank D has only gotten enriched rotifers so far. The larvae in Tank C are large and active, while the larvae in Tank D are still alive and active but not as large nor as active. I will add a little new brine shrimp napulii to both tanks today.

I may have made an amateurish error. I fed wild plankton to the brood stock tanks, since I has some large copepods and the fish really liked them, and I hated to just discard them. But I think the *A. ocellaris* are coming down with *Amyloodinium*. I pulled the pair out of BS 4, treated them to a fresh water bath, and set them up under copper treatment in a hospital tank. I may have to do the same with the pair in BS 3, which also holds the spawning dottybacks. This may be really bad news as I may have to set up about a half dozen treatment tanks if this affects the entire breeding system.

May 13, 1996, 4:10 PM

Busy days. Yesterday was Mother's Day and my little *P. fridmanis* didn't even send a card. Oh well, I didn't get any plankton for them yesterday either. I did go early this morning, 7 AM to get plankton. It is difficult these days for low tide is at mid day, which puts high tide either very early or very late. I have to give a talk to the West Palm Beach club tonight so I had to try the first of the falling tide, about 2 hours after slack high, early in the morning. Actually it worked out rather well as I found a good position that let the net tow in the current rather well. The plankton was of good quality.

The oldest two larvae are now 34 days old. They are strong juveniles and are feeding on plankton and a small amount of brine shrimp napulii. I imagine that they would also take tiny bits of shaved shrimp and small bits of dry food but I haven't had the time to experiment with this.

The next five larvae are 27 days old today and have picked up a significant amount of color. They are still not completely through metamorphoses but it appears very close. I observed them taking up positions in the corners of the tank and in the PVC pipe habitats that I placed in the tank. The 16 day old larvae are still quite numerous, still far too numerous to count, but there has been some mortality in the last day or two, perhaps 10 to 15. They are quite active and now spend some time near the bottom.

I have to watch the guts of the larval fish rather carefully to keep the food levels just right. Occasionally there will be a lot of food organisms in the tank, but they may be a bit to large for most of the larvae and some of the larvae may starve (this can happen in half a day) if the right size of food organism is not present. Rotifers or brine shrimp napulii can fill the gap if wild plankton is not on hand.

The last hatch that I have under culture is 10 days old today. This is the hatch that I split and placed in Tank C and Tank D. Tank C got wild plankton and D did not. There are larvae alive in both tanks so far, but the larvae in D are not as large nor as active as the larvae in C.

The male has eaten or otherwise disposed of the last spawn. This was a good large spawn and I don't know why he is not holding them through to hatch. Perhaps the feeding has not been right lately or perhaps the *Amyloodinium* and/ or *Cryptocaryon* has affected him, although I see no signs of an infection on either the male or female. Actually this may be a blessing in disguise because I was thinking of setting up a 20 gallon tank to rear the next batch and I really don't have the time to spend on it. I have to get back to working on the data book. I will do a lot of photography in the next few days to document all that I can about these rearing runs with the orchid dottyback.

May 15, 1996, 8:30 PM

The two oldest *P. fridmani* are now 36 days old. They are full juveniles and could be moved to a grow-out tank, if I had a grow-out tank for them. Very soon I will have to change things around to accommodate the young orchid dottybacks.

The five from the hatch of 4/15 are 29 days old. Two of these are now full color juveniles and the other three have settled and are in the process of developing their full color, but are still semitransparent with a strong orchid tint. The larvae from the hatch of 4/22 are also in the ten gallon tank and are now 18 days old and are late larvae. None of these has yet picked up the orchid color tint but they are gaining in size and appear normal for this time frame. I estimate that there are about 50 remaining at this point. I have been seeing about 2 to 4 dead larvae each day, some seem to stop feeding and just waste away, but there are now very few weak larvae in this group.

The youngest group is now 12 days old. They are in Tanks C and D, with tank C receiving plankton, rotifers, and brine shrimp, and tank D receiving only rotifers and brine shrimp to this point. I estimate that there are 25, in C and probably only 10 in D. The larvae in C are growing well and seem to be on the same track as the previous hatches. The larvae in D are only about half the size as the larvae in C and although less active, which may be a result of size as well as nutrition, they seem to be healthy to this point. Tomorrow I will try to sieve shaved shrimp below the 250 micron level and see if they will take these particles.

The pair spawned again today (or possibly yesterday?), so hatching should be on 5/19 (or 5/18) if he holds the eggs this time. I am in a quandary as to whether I should work with this next spawn or not. It is taking up a great deal of time and I have other projects that I have let slide during these rearing experiments. If I do make a rearing attempt, I will try again to bring some through without wild plankton. I could split the hatch again, and I do have an unused 20 gallon tank just sitting in the garage... and I can set it up on the back of the microscope table.... and who knows how many I can bring through in the vast recesses of a 20 gallon tank... Well, maybe just one more run.

May 17, 1996, 11:55 AM

Got plankton this AM. The tide was high at 9 AM so I had to be down at the bridge before 8 AM to get the best tidal flow. This meant that I had to drive on I 595 during the morning rush hour! And to think that some folks have to do that every morning. Anyway the plankton was good and it is a pretty day. This PM I will go to have a hole put in my 35 gallon half hex tank so that I can set up another tank for some of the juvenile *P. fridmani*. There are now 7 that have full color (from the 1st and 2nd post plankton spawns) and about 50 that are getting close. The colored juveniles are 38 and 31 days old today and the late larval juveniles are 20 days old. They seem to begin metamorphosis at about 26 to 28 days and complete it about day 30.

The 14 day old larvae in Tanks C and D are still doing well. There has been some mortality in both tanks but there are still a significant number alive in each tank, about 15 in tank C and abut 8 in tank D. The larvae in tank C are about twice as large as the ones in D, but the ones in D are still hanging in there at day 14! They have been fed mostly enriched rotifers, a little shaved shrimp, and few light feedings of brine shrimp. The fact that they have survived so far leads me to believe that I was correct about the fatty liver problems caused by the brine shrimp napulii. This is still conjecture, of course, because I have not yet examined the organs of the these larvae under the microscope. I would have to make squashes of both healthy and unhealthy larvae and compare the liver tissue squashes to be sure of this hypothesis. And even though this would give me a good indication of the status of the two livers, I still couldn't be positive until some histology was done on comparative livers.

The male is still holding the eggs from the spawn of 5/14 or 15. If the eggs are still there by Sat, 5/18 (Oh my gosh, that's tomorrow!), I will have to decide whether or not to set up the 20 gallon tank.

May 19, 1996, 3:30 PM

A beautiful Sunday afternoon and here I am fooling with fish tanks. Oh well, I will soon have enough data to hang up the rearing work for a while and concentrate on other things, like getting a book done. The plankton was very good today, I hit the incoming tide about an hour before peak and there was a lot of oceanic plankton.

I will move the two oldest juveniles today or tomorrow and free up that larval tank. They are 40 days old today. The 5 juveniles in the 10 gallon tank are 33 days old and the nearly metamorphosed large group of juveniles also in that tank are 22 days old. There has been no mortality in any of these groups recently and all looks well. I spent a lot of time last week doing photography and video so I will have the material for documentation.

There has been mortality in Tank C, quite a bit of mortality actually. There was a large patch of hydroids on the back wall and I saw two mid larval stage fish dead and stuck to a hydroid patch. There were also about 4 dead larvae scattered about the bottom of the tank. I don't know why they died, but I suspect that they brushed up against the hydroids, were stung, and escaped only to die later. It may have been another cause, but I suspect the hydroids.

There are about 7 larvae in Tank D, which have not been fed wild plankton to this date and are 16 days old. They have not been growing and I suspect that they would not have lasted much longer, so... I fed them some wild plankton today to see if they would survive. I know that this invalidated the experiment, but I was pretty sure that they would not survive much longer, and I didn't have the time to expend on trying to feed 7 larvae without wild plankton; so now they have a fighting chance.

The male is still holding the egg ball. It is a good bit smaller now but there is still about 100 or more eggs left. A few hatched last night and I siphoned out as many as I could and set them up in a 1 1/2 gallon jar. I did set up the 20 gallon tank in hopes that there will be a large enough hatch to justify the time and effort spent on the larger tank. If the egg ball is still there at about 5 or 6 tonight I will fill the tank and get it ready for a hatch. The temperature has been several degrees F higher in the breeding system in the last couple of weeks, 82 to 83 °F during the day rather than the 77 to 80 °F that it was during the last few months. This may be the reason that some of the eggs hatched last night instead of all of them hatching tonight.

May 20, 1996, 12:15 PM

The hatch came off last night as expected. The entire egg ball was not fertile, same as the last spawn. There were not nearly as many viable larvae as I wanted for the new 20 gallon larval tank, but enough to make a run for it. Today I will clean and change water in the breeding system and perhaps the next spawn will be better. If it comes off in

5 or 6 days, I can place it in the same tank. I ran the day old plankton through the 150 sieve and put the smallest fraction into the 20 gallon tank. There was some small zooplankton in this fraction, but I think it will work better with fresh plankton.

4:45 PM

I cleaned all five brood stock tanks and changed about 25% of the water in the system. I also ordered a UV unit that should be here in a day or two. I will install it before I put the three tanks with fish on the system. That way I may be able to keep the clownfish from coming down again with *Cryptocaryon*. I doubt that *Amyloodinium* was in the system, since if so, it would have hit the jawfish and bi-color dottyback by now.

The new larvae in the 20 gal are doing well, feeding on small plankton and enriched rotifers. Interestingly, there are a few larvae that are "bent", that is unable to straighten out from the curl that they had in the egg. They swim in tight little circles and are not able to capture food organisms. I have seen this condition in newly hatched clownfish that went past the time for hatch and then, when they did hatch, could not assume a normal swimming posture. Perhaps the increase in temperature in the breeding system is causing too rapid development in the embryos and they are past the optimum hatch time by the 4th night. However, I did get at least 25 good larvae, not many, but enough to continue the rearing run.

The *P. fridmani* spawned again today, about 2 PM. The egg ball looks good and so with the water change, I may get a good hatch. If so, I'll split the hatch with the new 20 gal. and Tank B, since I plan to move the two oldest juveniles to a brood stock tank in the near future.

May 21, 1996, 3:30 PM

A very rainy day, a low pressure area moved up from below Cuba and there is an incessant rain. Also my 90 year old mother was admitted to the hospital last night with a blood disorder. I skipped the plankton collection today. I did do some additional experimentation with the finely shaved and sieved shrimp and it seems to work quite well in that the particles are very small and do not readily settle out in the tank. They remain in the water column for quite some time and the larval fish appear to feed readily on them. There is no doubt that the juveniles take the small shrimp particles, but the pre metamorphic larvae move so fast that I have not actually seen a specific larva take a specific particle. However, the larvae swim actively among the particles and make repeated striking movements. I will have to do some more experimentation in this area. One detriment to this feeding technique is that the water apparently quickly picks up a bacteria load from the excess protein and requires change. I made a 50% change in the 10 gallon tank and put an exchange on Tanks C and D.

The 24 day old larvae in the 10 gallon tank are almost ready to metamorphose. They are about an inch long and are picking up the orchid coloration and look reddish in the tank. They are also moving to the bottom structures and are spending less time in the water column.

The 18 day old larvae in Tanks C and D are doing well. The mortality in tank C has ceased, perhaps because I got rid of the hydroid colony that was on the back wall of the tank. The larvae in tank D are active and feeding well. They have only had one feeding of plankton so far, and seem to have responded well. They have also received about three feedings of the shaved shrimp particles. They are still about half the size of the larvae in tank C.

The newest hatch is 2 days old today and they seem to be doing well. There are still a few larvae that are swimming in circles, but the others are feeding well.

May 24, 1996, 10:30 PM

The male ejected the egg ball (spawned on 5/20) from the den yesterday. I was lucky enough to look for the egg ball probably within 15 minutes of his ejection, otherwise I would not have known what happened. I saw the large female golden cleaner shrimp feeding on the egg ball and surmise that he ejected the eggs. I was able to get a good look at the eggs with a flashlight and my strongest reading glasses, and the eggs were all dead, no development of the embryos. I would assume that fertilization did take place and that the eggs did not survive under the male's care this time. I noticed that the male was away from the eggs frequently on this spawn. Perhaps he is not getting enough food to keep him on the spawn. Time was short these last few days and I have not been as regular with feeding as in the past. Mom is still in the hospital and we have been going there about twice a day. Also the temperatures in the tanks have been high, as I mentioned before, about 27 and 28 degrees C, maybe up to 29 in the late afternoon.

I have cut back on the plankton tows; the youngest larvae, now day 5 since hatch, are doing well with the plankton stretched out over three days and the older larvae are also doing well on a lesser amount of plankton. Also, the last plankton tows were very rich. I have also been experimenting with the tiny particles of shrimp and this technique seem to work well except for the tendency of the shrimp to foul the water. I think this can be avoided, however, but it will take more experimentation.

The largest group are now transforming into juveniles, their color is not yet intense, but quite a few of them are now taking up bottom residence and competing with the five oldest juveniles in the tank for living space. All other larval tanks are doing well.

May 26, 1996, 11:15 AM

Well here it is Memorial Day weekend and I am sorting plankton, feeding yeast and algae to rotifers, feeding rotifers to fish, feeding fish, cleaning tanks, etc. Which is one of the problems with fish culture, there is always a pressing task to perform. But today I will move the first two juveniles, 47 days old today, to a brook stock tank, which makes it all worthwhile, Wow, they are actually big enough to sell at 50 days!, but I'm glad that I'm no longer a commercial fish farmer. I can hang up the apron whenever I wish, at least until the rearing bug bites again. And there was a spawn in the male fridmani's den this morning, a nice big egg ball again. Perhaps this time he will bring the spawn to hatch and if so, I guess I will add them to the 20 gallon tank that is already set up. The hatch will be on Wednesday, 5/29. The larvae in that tank are doing very well with all that space to grow, but there are only about 30 from that spawn. They are 7 days old today and will be 10 days old when the next spawn hatches, and it is pushing it to put them in the same tank with 10 day old larvae, but I will try it since it is a really big tank, relatively speaking.

The late larvae and early juveniles are mixed in the 10 gallon tank. About one third of the 29 day old larvae have metamorphosed into juveniles and the others are almost there. I will take some more video footage today.

The 23 day old larvae in Tanks C and D are a mixed bag. There are not many in either tank. The larvae in tank

C received wild plankton from day one and are large late stage larvae at this point. There are not too many of them, about 4 or 5, since it was a small hatch and more significantly, the hydroids got a foothold (polyp hold?) in that tank and killed quite a few larvae. The larvae in tank D did not receive wild plankton until May 19, day 16. There are about 5 or 6 surviving at this point, day 23, and they seem to be doing well, but are still in the mid larval stage, a little over half the size of the larvae in tank C. Evidently wild plankton does provide important and essential nutrients to the developing orchid dottyback larvae. I will keep feeding them rotifers and wild plankton, plus a little brine shrimp napulii, and see how they do, they seem healthy and normal at this point, if a little stunted.

I got the 30 watt UV sterilizer hooked up yesterday and it seems to be working well. Of course I can't determine the kill rate for sure, but I hope it creates a sterile barrier between the tanks on that system. It does seem to push the temperature in the system up about a degree F to 83 - 84 °F over the 82 - 83 °F that the system has been running since the weather got hot. This may also be a factor in the declining success of the *P. fridmani* hatches.

May 29, 1996, 3:30 PM

Since the last entry on 5/26 I learned that the reason the temperature in the breeding system is rising is not the new UV filter. The air conditioner on this side of the house is leaking coolant and the room temperature is rising about 4 degrees. This will be fixed tomorrow, but we did recharge the compressor and the temperatures are back down in the breeding system to under 82 °F. Perhaps the next spawn will hold. The last spawn, due to hatch on 4/29 (today) disappeared yesterday. That makes about 3 spawns in a row that have failed to progress to hatching. Couldn't run a commercial operation with that loss.

Took one of the 43 day old juveniles to the May meeting of the Florida Marine Aquarium Society for the fish raffle. This was the "first distribution of *P. fridmani* that were spawned and reared in the continental United States." (It amuses me sometimes when folks claim "firsts" by placing irrelevant or unimportant qualifications on a claim to pump up the importance of that claim. Like, the TV station that screeches "We were the first to break the story!", when every other station had the news 2 minutes later. Or "We have the biggest private collection of dried beatles in Choctaw county." Which may be true, but is it significant? But then look at the popularity of the *Guinness Book of Records*. I guess being first, even with qualifications and nonsignificance can be very important.) For the record, as far as I know, I was the third to rear the orchid dottyback, behind Robert Brons and Bill Addison (I don't know who was first), but I think I was the first to do it at home, by myself, in a converted bathroom, which I think adds a certain pizazz to my position.

I had placed two metamorphosed juveniles from tank C into the big 55 gallon grow-out/invertebrate tank a couple of days ago. I moved all the fish from tank C because the hydroids kept killing them off one by one. I found two juveniles and about 5 or 6 late larvae in that tank, the juveniles were moved to the 55 and the other larvae were moved to tank D. I was a bit worried because I had had a large toadfish, *Opsanus beta,* that had gotten into that tank as a post larvae along with the live rock, and grew up eating a few small clownfish and I don't know what else.

I thought he might have gone to fish heaven (or hell), when that tank was drained because of a power failure and an algae plugged siphon break hole. This event did kill a beautiful pair of blue striped clowns that Alec Brooks had given to me, but not the toad fish. I saw him in the tank one night after I had placed the two tiny orchid dottybacks in the tank. I thought for sure he had taken the little guys since I never saw them after putting them in the tank. I caught the toadfish on a tiny hook baited with a piece of shrimp and removed him from that tank yesterday. Then today I observed both little orchid dottybacks at either end of the tank. I thought they were too fast and smart for an old toad fish.

Almost all the *P. fridmani* in the 10 gallon tank are now juveniles. There are a few, perhaps 10, that are still reddish late larvae, but all the rest now have their purple coloration. There is a situation now in that tank, where the faster, bigger juveniles get more food than the smaller juveniles and the larvae that have not yet metamorphosed. I may move some of the smaller fish and put them in a separate tank to give them a better chance at growth.

The ecology of a larval rearing tank changes gradually as the fish grow. It starts off representative of a micro plankton environment, with microscopic algae cells and macro sized rotifers, plankton, and tiny larval fish. As the days pass, the fish and their food organisms get larger, bacteria populations increase, algae grows on the sides and bottom, and the tank ecology changes from a sort of open ocean planktonic environment to a more benthic, near shore, more eutrophic environment with larger organisms. Then, as the fish near metamorphosis, a very significant change takes place. The tank loses it's planktonic nature and becomes benthic, especially if substrate is introduced to provide shelter for the transforming fish. When this happens, the fish entering and passing through metamorphosis have a great advantage over the fish still in the mid or late larval stage. The tank no longer supports high levels of planktonic food organisms, in fact very few plantonic organisms survive for very long in the tank, and the growth of the late developing late larval and post larval fish is further stunted by the lack of proper sized food organisms and by the presence of the larger fish. Many of these late developers do survive, but their survival can be enhanced by moving them to a different tank, one that is more representative of the environment that is optimum to their stage of development.

The larvae in tank D are still doing well and I should get about 12 to 15 juveniles from this batch. The larvae in the 20 gallon tank are 10 days old and have grown well, I estimate that there are about 15 in that tank. I never did get another hatch to put in that tank and it doesn't look as if I will get another hatch in time to add them to that run. I may move the few in the 20 to another tank and set it up again if I get another good hatch soon. I have cut back on the plankton gathering because it takes up so much time and I don't really have a lot of fish in the plankton feeding stage right now. I think I can squeeze by another couple of days without getting the plankton. Of course this will be hard on the toadfish. I am holding him in a jar for now, I plan to release him to the inlet when I get plankton again. After all, he came from the wild and it's not like releasing a non native fish or a diseased fish. It's hard to kill a healthy fish that you've kept for 6 months, even if it is a fish eating monster.

6

June 1996 -

Trials and Tribulations

June 5, 1996, 2:45 PM

Everything is rolling along since the last entry. Unfortunately, the male is still losing the eggs on the 3rd day after spawn. I don't know why because the eggs seem to be developing normally for the first three days, I can even see the eyes developing, but then on the third day the egg ball seems to get smaller and smaller and then disappears completely. It may be that the eggs are hatching early, during the day, but I don't think so since it would be a full day and a half early. The temperatures are still a couple of degrees F higher, 82 to 83.5 °F, than they were during the better hatches of the last three months. I will turn off the UV unit for this next spawn and see if the temp drops and if the eggs survive.

My plankton trips are now about every 3 to 4 days instead of every other day. Most of the larvae are now juveniles and they feed on shaved shrimp, brine shrimp napulii, and even dry food, so the need for plankton is much less. The last hatch of *P. fridmani* are now 17 days old and have done well in the "big" 20 gallon tank. They are almost an inch long now and zoom about the tank. The

other, older, fish are almost all juveniles at this point, except for the ones that were not given plankton in the first
16 days. They are now 33 days old, and while the others
from that hatch that had plankton in the early days are
now juveniles, the original fish from larval Tank D are still
late larvae, but have some color and will soon become juveniles.

Barb took some video footage of the plankton towing
process this morning and I now have all the information,

The 53 micron, one half meter plankton net used for collecting copepods and other plankton. A long pole is used to hold the net away from
the barnacle laden seawall.

35 mm slides, and video footage needed to describe the rearing process. I do want to do one more run with a large hatch in the 20 gallon tank, but if this does not happen, I still have all the necessary documentation. I will continue to make entries in this rearing journal, but they will become more sporadic unless I can start a major rearing run in the near future.

June 6, 1996, 10:00 AM

The *P. fridmani* are spawning at this moment. At first they would spawn in the afternoon, but now they seem to spawn at mid morning. I turned off the UV unit and this may serve to lower the temperature in the breeding tank. We will see if this makes a difference in the success of this spawn.

June 7, 1996, 3:00 PM

The temperature in the breeding systems is down a bit, 81.5 °F at noon. The male is still holding a big egg ball. The eggs are due to hatch on 6/10, so we shall see....

June 10, 1996, 9:00 PM

The temperature in the breeding systems has been below 82 °F for the entire 4 days of incubation. The male is still holding the egg ball so I am sure that there will be a hatch tonight, most likely within an hour. I can see the egg ball fairly well with the powerful reading glasses (2.5) and the flashlight and it doesn't look as if many of the eggs are in the eyed stage, meaning that most of the eggs did not develop. I don't know if the problem is in the fertilization or in development. I think that only about 10% of the eggs have developed, but we shall see...

I took 9 late larval and 2 early juvenile fish from the 20 gallon tank this afternoon to make it ready for the hatch tonight. These fish were only 22 days old and already through the larval stage into the early juvenile stage. This is the most rapid larval development I have had with *P. fridmani*. I did not feed them much plankton either, but the large tank did hold a lot of food organisms for such a small number of larvae. I think that there were less than 25 that went into that tank and many of these were poor hatch larvae that had no chance of survival. The larval environment, water and food, have a great effect on larval development.

The other hatches are doing very well, I have moved a pair, in one case, a trio, into each brood stock tank. The remainder are still in the larval tanks. They are almost ready to sell. Another couple of weeks, providing that they are not too stunted by the small tanks. I may move them all into the 55, but it would be a bear to get them out of the rocks in that tank, so I have resisted the temptation so far.

June 11, 1996, 10:30 AM

Another lesson learned! Geeze, when am I going to stop learning lessons? Hmmmm. On second thought I guess learning lessons is better than the alternative. Anyway, I wasn't sure how many larvae were going to hatch last night, so although I moved the 11 fish from the 20 gallon tank, I didn't take the time or trouble to clean the tank. I siphoned the bottom and removed all but about 2 inches of water so that I could catch the fish in a bowl rather than a net (a net is bad news for even a late larval fish) and then left the tank as it was, since it wasn't completely overrun with bottom growth, until I could see what the hatch would produce. They came off as predicted about 45 minutes after dark and the hatch was not strong, maybe as many as 75 larvae. I siphoned out all that I could into a gallon jar, three times, and moved the larvae into the 20 gallon tank by lowering the jar into the tank and gently pouring out the water into the tank, a technique that I have often used. The tank was about half full at the end of the larval transfer and with a flashlight I could see a fair number of larvae in the tank.

This morning when I looked into the tank, I saw only about 3 larvae. Where had they gone? Either the larvae were of such poor quality that they all died shortly after hatch, an unlikely situation, or something had taken the larvae during the night. I had not added the dose of streptomycin to the tank yet, but this is typically added the morning after hatch. This tank had received wild plankton, not a great amount, most of the larval food had been enriched rotifers and brine shrimp napulii, but there had been enough wild plankton to create a few barnacles and other fouling growth on the bottom and sides of the tank. And a growth of hydroids, which I belatedly found on the back side of the tank. There were also a few chaetognaths that had survived the water removal and bottom siphoning.

I examined the bottom growths under the dissecting microscope and found some hydroids hidden in the algae as well as the large patch on the side. If the larvae have a start of a few days to a week on rotifers before wild plankton is introduced, then they have a jump on the development of plankton introduced predators and are able to keep ahead of their growth and in most cases, these planktonic predators are kept in check by feeding only the fraction below 150 or 250 microns for the first couple of weeks. But it is a mistake to introduce newly hatched fish larvae to a larval tank that has an established growth of organisms from past wild plankton feedings. Duhhh.

June 14, 1996, 3:50 PM

The pair spawned again on 6/12 at 4:00 PM. It is a large egg ball and the male is attentive so it may hatch on the evening of 6/16. I will be ready with a clean and newly set up 20 gallon tank, so if we do get a good hatch, I may be able to rear a large number of larvae.

I moved all the fish out of the 10 gallon tank this morning and set them up in a half full 20 with a couple of live rocks and the PVC pipe habitats that were in the 10. There were 66 fish in the tank. This represents maybe a half to a third of the total of number of larvae that were placed in the tank. Whatever the percentage of survival, 66 juveniles from a 10 gallon tank is not too bad, especially for a newly cultured species. There are about 20 juveniles in larval tank D that are 40 days old and 11 in larval tank C that are 26 days old, all of these having transformed to juveniles by day 25, a most rapid growth rate. No recent spawns have produced any hatched larvae that have survived so there are no younger larvae. I would like to try one more large, health hatch, but I am also anxious to get deeper into writing the book on rearing marine fish.

June 16, 1996, Fathers Day, 1:15 PM

The kids (35 and 32, no longer kids) and two of the grand kids will be over soon, but I have a few minutes to catch up here. The spawn was gone by the third day. I watched it carefully and only a very few eggs showed signs of development. I don't know why the eggs have stopped developing normally in the last two months. The possibilities are nutrition in the female, water quality, male care of the eggs, development of some bacterial or parasitic infection in the female or in the eggs, temperature, or some other factor that I am not aware of. I should do a relatively complete water change on that system. I have changed about 5% of the system water every one or two weeks, although lately, since I have been using new water for the algal cultures, I might not have hit this level of exchange. The pH is staying above 8.0, I haven't checked the nitrate for some time and it may have crept up. A major water change would be good for the system.

The juvenile *P. fridmani* are all doing very well. Color and activity is strong, I have about 100 juveniles from about 4 spawns of last spring. They are quite hardy, I have lost very few after the 20th day of development, scarcely more than 5 or 6 that I can remember. This species would be an excellent choice for culture, small in size, spawns readily, hardy larvae and juveniles, rapid growth, and most important, a high value species, ideal for small scale culture.

June 18, 1996, 1:20 PM

Disaster struck over the weekend. The 14 juvenile orchid dottybacks in larval tank D were doing fine on Saturday, although I admit that I did not examine the tank very closely, but there were no dead fish or any that were obviously in distress. Then on Sunday afternoon there were suddenly 11 dead fish on the bottom. I suspected *Amyloodinium* and I removed the 4 survivors and placed them in copper treatment. The dead fish showed no *Amyloodinium* cysts on the body, but did have bacterial damage on the caudal and pectoral fins. This may have been secondary infections as a result of *Amyloodinium* damage. Of the 4 survivors, one died soon after placement in a treatment tank and one showed extensive caudal fin damage this morning. I doubt that it will survive, but I did add neomycin to the treatment tank. One must be ever vigilant with tanks of small fish for disease and death are always only hours away.

There are no other problems with any of the other juveniles. They are scattered through the tank systems in twos and threes and the rest concentrated in two tanks. All seems well at this point.

June 22, 1996, 2:10 PM

The pair spawned on 6/19 and this should hatch on 6/23 if the eggs are viable. I have been checking the egg ball and it still looks good, it is still large and the male is attentive, but I won't know for sure until tomorrow. If this is a good hatch, I'll try it in the 20 to see how a large hatch survives in this large tank. The juveniles are now 76, 67, 56, 48 and 34 days old. The pairs, the trio and the 9 individuals in the big, rock filled 55 gallon tank are growing faster and have better color than the 65 juveniles in the half filled 20 gallon tank, which is to be expected. I don't have a good grow-out set up for these fish. The smallest juveniles in the 20 are not growing much at all. I will have to begin selling and giving these guys away soon or I will certainly begin to lose them due to poor conditions.

June 24, 1996, 5:30 PM

I stabilized the 20 gallon grow-out tank with a small sponge filter to pull out floating particles and also added a bag of protein resin to lower the organic content of the water. The fish look better but many of them have nipped tails due to aggressive interactions. Most of them are now large enough to sell and I will start selling them tomorrow at the Florida Marine Aquarium Society swap meet in Miami. After that I'll sell a few to various aquarium shops.

The hatch last night was very poor. I placed them in larval tank C and there are probably only about 20 or so that seem viable. I have added enriched rotifers and a bit of algae culture to the tank and we will see how they do. I may or may not get wild plankton for this hatch depending on my schedule and the number of strong larvae.

I don't know why at least 95% of the eggs do not develop. The ones that do develop go through to hatch and even though they are not as strong as they should be, it does show that fertilization occurs, thus the fertilizing capacity of the male is probably not the limiting factor. Most eggs show no development or death at a very early stage of development. The most likely problem is with the quality of the eggs delivered by the female. If all her eggs were good, then it seems that more of them should develop all the way to hatch as long as a few do so.

The other possibilities are that water quality is so poor that the eggs do not develop or that there is a bacterial or microspordian infection in the female that gets into the eggs or that a bacterial infection destroys most of the eggs. I don't buy that last one, if there was a bacterial problem external to the eggs that destroyed 98% of them, then there is little chance that the remaining 2% would survive. I've got to take the time to do a complete water quality testing on that system, but then I do change a lot of water fairly often.

The female looks very good and eats very well. I doubt that there is an internal infection in her that destroys the eggs, although I have seen a microsporidean infection in clownfish that acts this way. My best guess, through the process of elimination, is that the nutrition of the female is lacking something that the eggs need. I have been feeding the pair on shrimp shavings, brine shrimp napulii, and two types of dry food. I think the first thing I'll do is to change back to the original brand of dry food that I was using at first and see if that makes a difference.

June 25, 1996, 4:15 PM

The hatch was better than I thought. It looked as if only a few had hatched but after a day in the larval tank it looks as if there are at least 50 and maybe up to 75 larvae in the tank. They are feeding on enriched rotifers, and today, at 2 days old, they are swimming strong and feeding well. These tanks have one 4 foot daylight 40 watt fluorescent bulb about a 10 inches above the tank. This seemed to be enough for the larvae and there was good survival at this level of luminescence. I put a high intensity, two bulb, mini fluorescent light over this tank to increase the lighting for video taping and I was surprised to see the larvae quickly gather near the surface and greatly increase their feeding and swimming activity. I will leave this light in place over the tank for this run and see if the larvae grow or survive better than before. The run in the 20 gallon tank that grew so fast also had a much stronger light over that tank.

I have to take a two or three day trip to Birmingham this weekend to see the other two grandkids. It is time to do this and this is the best weekend available. I will start the larvae on plankton just before we leave and hope that they will make it through until my return. I will also have to remove the high intensity light over the larval tank during those days because it does not have a timer on it.

Tonight I'll sell 8 of the juveniles at the Miami club's swap meet, I'll also give away 8 since I had promised a few to friends. It should be fun, I've given them all names of Greek and Roman gods.

June 26, 1996, 5:40 PM

All went well last night. Apollo, Bacchus, Calypso, Diana, Eros, Flora, Glaucus, and Hera all found new homes in hobbyist's tanks. The silent auction was a good idea. Everyone had a chance to bid on them and they all went for 10 to 13 dollars each. The retail price, albeit for a bit larger fish, is anywhere from 25 to 70 dollars so they all got a good deal and we made a little on it too. Actually, counting all my time, trouble and effort, I should have gotten $2,000.00 each for them, but I guess that would be a bit steep.

I should have let this last batch of about 50 larvae just go down the drain. I doubt that they will survive my being gone for 4 days this weekend. But could I do that, Noooooo. I had to go get plankton today in hopes of pulling them through until I get back on Tuesday, July 2. Summer plankton is no fun, I had forgotten about that. Even right close to the ocean inlet on high tide, the plankton is chock full of brown diatoms. These diatoms are tiny little spears (pennate diatoms) about as long as a rotifer and they don't settle out well. The sieved plankton looks like coffee and the copepods and their napulii are all tied up in the diatoms and it is impossible to separate them. The best thing I have found to do is to concentrate the plankton into a quart bowl and let it settle for a few hours. Don't go too long or the plankton dies and if you forget it and leave it overnight, Skunk City! Nothing smells as bad as rotten plankton. Anyway, after a couple of hours, decant the plankton into a bowl and leave all the diatoms that do settle out in the bottom of the bowl. The results are not rich with tiny napulii or even large copepods, but it is sufficient to feed a few small tanks. Even after a couple of hours, however, there is still a dense mix of diatoms in the water.

June 27, 1996, 11:45 AM

Hoo Boy, Summertime plankton is bad news. A dense, coffee color mix of diatoms and only a small amount of crustacean larvae. It will settle out almost completely but it takes overnight to do it. There are some copepods and tiny crustacean larvae that do accumulate in the almost clear upper layers of the settled plankton. If the bowl is shallow enough, there is enough oxygen in the upper portion to keep the critters alive and there are enough zooplankers to feed a small tank, perhaps up to 20 gallons. Good enough for a small hobbyist scale rearing, but bad news for a commercial operation. I had the same problems in Tampa Bay back in the early 70's and also in the Keys in the early 80's.

Everything is set up for a four day trip. The larger fish should be fine since Andrea will come in and feed twice and maybe the larvae will make it, we'll see. They are 4 days old and are doing very well so far.

7

July 1996 -

A New Technique

July 2, 1996, 10:30 AM

Back from four days in Birmingham. A good trip, nice to get away for a little while and visit Steve and Leigh and the grand kids we don't get to see very often. We went through Montgomery to avoid the horrendous Atlanta traffic created by the upcoming Olympics and ran right into much worse traffic jams in Montgomery and Troy. It seems that we somehow became part of the precession of running the Olympic torch through southern Alabama. We spent over 3 hours in first gear crawling along through vast assemblages of folks waving American flags by the side of the road. At first it was sort of fun, we waved to everybody and they waved back, I don't know who they thought we were, but after two hours it began to get a little tiresome.

Anyway, everything survived, except for the *P. fridmani* larvae. There are about 10 left, and these are not well. They are weak and small and not worth a plankton run.

5:00 PM

Actually, now that I've fed some enriched rotifers and brine shrimp napulii, I see that there are about 20 to 25 larvae left alive in the tank and that they are not weak and drifting after all. They are 8 days old today and they look a bit small, but they do feed on day old brine shrimp napulii and now with the extra light on the top of the tank, they are up near the surface and are feeding strongly. I'm not sure what I'll do at this point.

The other tanks came through fine, no mortality, the *P. fridmani* pair is spawning as I write this. I wanted to video the courtship again, but wasn't able to get the camera together today. I'll try on the next spawn.

July 3, 1996, 1:30 PM

The latest larvae are 9 days old at this time, probably about 20 of them left. They are not growing well but they are still alive and feeding actively. I know that I can bring them through if I just go get a plankton tow every couple of days for the next 10 to 15 days. Since there are so few larvae, I might even be able to get by with only one tow every three days, maybe only three more infusions of plankton would do the trick. It evidently is not necessary for the entire diet of the larvae to consist of wild plankton, only some relatively small portion during the time between day 8 and day 20 has to be wild plankton.

I wonder what it is in the wild plankton that makes survival possible. At this point it is not necessary to know what that essential substance is, only to be able to provide it at the right time in an acceptable amount. Different species seem to need "element X" in variable amounts, clownfish can get by without it, or at least with only the amount that is found in rotifers and brine shrimp, and the gray and

French angelfish seem to require that almost their entire diet, at least up to about day 12 be nothing but wild plankton. I doubt that it is a basic protein, amino acid, or starch of some type; also it doesn't seem that it would be a mineral, which leaves mostly some of the fatty acids and, of course, some of the vitamins. In the case of the angelfish, the pattern of movement of the prey organisms also seems important in eliciting the feeding response in the larvae. There is a lot of research to be done here, and I'm afraid that I will have to leave this for other inquiring minds.

P. fridmani grow fast! Now at 86 and 77 days, the largest of the oldest juveniles are about 50 mm or 2 inches long. Whenever two were set up in one tank, one juvenile is always considerably larger than the other and has the bottom rays of the caudal fin elongated into a sort of a point. These appear to be the males. In the one tank where I had set up a trio, I think only two remain in that tank, but I can't be sure yet. In the 55 that is full of live rock and has only 9 juveniles (I only put a few in that tank because I knew that it would be almost impossible to get them out), only one has the really distinct elongated bottom caudal and he is considerably larger than the others. There are two or three others that are almost as large, but they don't have the elongated ventral caudal rays and are definitely subservient to the largest juvenile.

There is one dominant fish in the 20 gallon tank that has about 40 juveniles. Growth and size differences are not as great in this tank as in the others with only two or a few fish. It would appear that sexual determination is dependent on the social structure of the group, with one fish in each group becoming the larger dominant male and the others developing into females. Thus to develop a pair, all that is apparently required is to obtain two small fish that have not yet become sexually mature and one will develop into a male and the other a female, just as in the clownfish. I don't know what would happen if a small, immature fish was placed with an adult female.

July 8, 1996, 10:00 AM

Well we had busy Fourth of July weekend. Mom's 90th birthday was on the 5th and everyone was over on the 4th for ribs, chicken and fireworks and I towed Winston in a plastic boat behind the kayak for three miles. And, of course, one day, the 6th, was devoted to dottyback culture. All the tanks were cleaned and the outside rotifer culture was rejuvenated. I siphoned the accumulated crud from the bottom of the tank, removed 5 gallons of old water and added new water and adjusted the salinity to about 32 ppt. One of the outside cultures was in a place where roof run-off could hit it in a hard rain and so this culture was almost all fresh water by now. I cleaned that one up completely and retired it. All I need to supplement the inside tray cultures is one good outside culture anyway.

Salinity adjustment on the inside systems is a continuing task. I use a fan on the sumps to speed evaporation since this also helps greatly on temperature control but it also requires a lot of make up water. Since accumulation of some phosphate and nitrate is not a problem with a fish culture operation, I can use a PVC pipe charcoal filter to remove the chlorine and since it's a fairly big pipe, most of the chloramine as well. In fact, I'm topping off the 110 gallon grow-out system right now, I better go check on it before I get water all over the floor....

No problem, it's on a mere trickle so I have at least 15 minutes yet. (Wow, that little stone crab that I couldn't get rid of last fall is now almost as big as my fist! I hope it can't catch orchid dottybacks.) Actually, this is where I could have a big problem. It's easy to forget you're filling a tank when there is 15 minutes or more to get engrossed in doing something else. And then 45 minutes later, Disaster!

Speaking of disaster, this week opens up with Bertha churning away at Puerto Rico. I hope Bill Addison at C-Quest comes though with little or no damage. Bertha has apparently set her course directly toward South Florida and my little fish room. She might be here in three or four days, so do I buy a gasoline powered generator or not? Do I spend three or four hundred dollars to make sure that the fish stay alive if the electric is out for a few days, or do I take my chances and hope that Bertha heads out to sea before she gets here? I'll check generator prices later today on my way to get plankton.

There was a good, not great, just good, hatch on Saturday night, 7/6, from the spawn of 7/2. I could see a lot of little eyes in the egg ball on Saturday, so I knew that there would be a decent hatch that night and I cleaned up the 20 gallon tank for this hatch. Of course, Bertha may mess up any chance of getting them through, but I figure I'd try anyway. I really want to try rearing a decent number in a larger tank before I hang up the siphon and spend all my time on the computer.

The hatch came off well and I collected them with a siphon into a gallon jar and then carefully emptied the jar into the half full 20 gallon tank. I collected almost all the larvae in three jar fulls and the next morning there were at least 200 good larvae in the tank. There were still a lot of eggs that were bad, at least 50%, perhaps 75%. I got enough larvae for a good rearing attempt in the 20 gallon tank, but if this was a commercial operation, I would really be working at figuring out why the majority of the eggs were not good.

The new larvae are 2 days old today and I am going to get some wild plankton just before high tide at 2:30 PM. Larvae from the last hatch are 14 days old today. They have had only one feeding of wild plankton at about day 2 and now at day 15 they are still small, they look like day 6 or 7 larvae, and mortality is increasing. They have had only rotifers and brine shrimp the last 12 days. I will give them some wild plankton today and see what happens.

8:40 PM

Big Bertha is still heading our way, and packing 90 mph winds at this point. She is still just off Puerto Rico and if her course holds she could be here on Friday or Saturday, just 4 or 5 days away. I did buy a generator today. There were only 6 left at Costco and while we stood there debating about whether or not to buy one, two more were quickly snapped up, so we went ahead and got one. Now at least I'll have lights, pumps and air if Bertha disrupts the electric for a few days.

The plankton was rather good, especially for summer plankton. There was a lot of algae in the water, even some great green globs, planktonically speaking, and a lot of the pennate diatoms, also a good number of centrate diatoms. This algae tends to settle out a lot faster than the heavy diatom load in the previous tows and there is now much more zooplankton in the tows. A lot of small copepods and copepod napulii and other minute crustacea were in the tows and the new *P. fridmani* larvae are eating well. The 15 day old larvae are in hog, er, copepod heaven. Their guts turned white with copepods and they are buzzing about the little tank feeding avidly. I have 5 gallons of plankton bubbling for tomorrow, and Wed. or Thursday, depending

on Bertha's plans, I will get another couple of tows to hopefully hold them over the few days of troubled weather.

July 9, 1996, 10:30 PM

Looks like we dodged the bullet. Bertha seems to be
headed to the north of us so all we should get, if anything,
is a bit of wind and rain. It's still too early to tell for sure,
however, so we have another day of uncertainty.

The 16 day old larvae were saved by the plankton, they
grew noticeably overnight and there are about 6 or 7 remaining. I caught one little late larval fish in the plankton
net and, soft soul that I am, I put him in tank C along with
the dottybacks. I think it's probably a little grunt, but we'll
see. The 3 day old larvae in the 20 gallon tank are doing
well. It's hard to see them in the plankton rich tank, but
every larvae that I observe is feeding well and very active.

The pair of *P. fridmani* spawned again yesterday, 7/8, I
haven't checked the eggs yet today, but if they are good
they will hatch on Friday, 7/12. I may put them in with the
last hatch in the 20 gallon tank. I'll have to be careful not to
overload this tank. Too many larvae in one tank reduces
the chances of getting many through.

A "seat of the pants" marine fish breeder always has to
be thinking, and curious, and willing to follow up on wild
ideas if they seem to make sense. I had a V8® for lunch the
other day and got to wondering what would happen if one
put a little V8® in a culture bottle and added rotifers. So I
did. The water turned a sort of cloudy reddish color and
the puree from the juice settled to the bottom. Looking at
the solution under the dissecting microscope showed a lot
of vegetable fragments from fairly large, over 250 microns,
to smaller than 10 microns. The rotifers seemed to like it,
their guts soon turned a reddish brown color. This morn-

ing the rotifers were still doing quite well, most had eggs and the culture still smelled good. So I set up a tray culture with V8® and rotifers. I put the juice through a 500 micron screen and pulled out a lot of small carrot chunks and some of the larger vegetable fragments. The culture water now looks a reddish brown. If they do well on this culture medium, it may be an easy and inexpensive way to culture rotifers. Should be better than yeast, but perhaps not as good as live algae. Barb pointed out that adding a little of the nutritious yeast that carries B vitamins as well may be a good addition, so I will try this as well. The rotifers will still have to be enriched for 4 to 8 hours with a source of Omega 3 fatty acids, Super Selco, Selco, or Selcon, to give the larval fish the best nutritional base, but who knows, it may even supply the "missing ingredient" found in plankton. Fat chance, but worth a try. It may, however, make rearing decent rotifers much easier.

July 10, 1996, 11:00 AM

I've been trying to come up with a good motto for fish breeders. Some of the possibilities are "It's always something", "If everything is going good, you've obviously overlooked something", "Expect the worst", "Disaster is right around the corner", "Mother Nature is a Bitch", and "If anything can possibly go wrong, it will." I'm sure that there are many other candidates for a working motto but any of these seem suitable.

Last night I pulled the air on the brine shrimp hatch to allow it to settle before pulling off the hatched napulii, and I forgot to go back and do it, so this morning all the brine shrimp are dead and I have none to feed. Not a great disaster, but an annoying one. Then I looked in Larval Tank C that has, had, 15 juvenile *P. fridmani*, and noticed one dead on the bottom and all the others in great stress. A few hanging in the water column and the others on the bottom respiring rapidly. They also appeared rather thin. Now these were in great shape yesterday, strong and colorful, feeding well and no sign of any problems. The exchange from the system into the tank had slowed to trickle because of detritus build up in the valve, but this is not unusual, nor is it a problem since there is an air release in the tank and there was still a strong trickle into the 8 gallon tank.

Something this quick is either an overlooked case of *Amyloodinium* or an occurrence of dreaded Toxic Tank Syndrome. The observed thinness of the fish led me to believe that it was toxic tank syndrome, and so I quickly removed the fish and placed them in clean saltwater and added a dose of streptomycin and neomycin, about 400 mg of each in 3 gallons of saltwater.

I examined the dead and moribund fish and saw no sign of *Amyloodinium* or any other external parasite. The fins were a bit frayed and showed some sign of bacterial erosion at the edges, but nothing that in itself would cause great stress and death, since the same level of frayed fins can be observed in some fish that are in the 20 gallon tank. In my opinion, *P. fridmani* is subject to the same toxic tank syndrome that often affects juvenile clownfish, neon gobies, and angelfish in closed systems. Two more have died since the move at 9:00 AM and I expect one or two more will go during the day, but I think the other 11 will survive.

This same thing happened to 13 juveniles that were in larval tank D a couple of months ago, but I did not catch it in time and all but two died. I suspected toxic tank in that first instance but was not able to observe it in the early stages and thus was not sure. The best defense against toxic tank syndrome is to keep the tanks clean, keep biological filtration to a minimum, keep a good water exchange rate going, observe the fish frequently for signs of the disorder, keep the fish in many small tanks rather than one big one, and move fish though the system to market or disbursement as fast as possible. Therefore, I will have to start selling some of these little guys as soon as possible.

I'll also have to clean out the toxic tank and wipe it down with chlorine water to remove as much of the bacterial contamination as possible.

The V8® rotifer cultures are coming along. The rotifers are growing and reproducing. The red flocculent material on the bottom of the cultures is growing rapidly also. Also there is a wild culture of some sort of very tiny ciliates developing in the culture. They zoom through the culture with great speed. I'll have to look at them through the compound microscope. The V8® culture method may work but I think it will require siphoning the bottom of the culture vessels frequently and certainly condensing the rotifers over a 53 micron sieve.

The youngest *P. fridmani* larvae are doing well. I'll have to get plankton again either tomorrow or Friday. Bertha has turned to the North enough to miss us completely, except for perhaps a little wind tonight, so I should be able to get plankton at high tide sometime in the next two days.

July 11, 1996, 10:30 AM

RATS! RATS! RATS! RATS! RATS! I'm sorry, I have this tendency to swear violently when things don't go right. I don't know what it is about swearing, I mean it's just a word or two, a verbal or mental exclamation with some reference to a religious, excretory, or procreative function that usually has absolutely no meaning or reference to the situation at hand (depending, of course, on what you

may have just stepped upon). Just words, one would think
that any words would do, but it has to be certain words. In
my case it is a loud verbalization of the common name for
a group of rodents. Whatever, it does make one feel better
for some reason, just one of the great mysteries of life.
Which brings me to another great mystery, the Toxic Tank
Syndrome. I lost 7 of the 15 juvenile dottybacks that were
in larval tank C yesterday. The remaining 8 are doing great
this morning, feeding on brine shrimp nauplii and looking
normal despite the ordeal of yesterday. I have no doubt
that if I had left them in that tank yesterday, despite water
change, that I would have lost most, if not all of them. Yet
today, the survivors show little effect from this ordeal.

The most probable cause for this syndrome, in my
opinion, is external bacterial toxins. The bacteria, most
likely *Vibrio*, do not attack the fish directly, but bloom in
the aquarium in numbers large enough that the toxins that
they discharge into the environment are strong enough to
affect and kill the fish. I noticed that some of the most affected fish yesterday showed evidence of paralysis. On one
side of the fish the pectoral fin was active, but the pectoral
fin on the other side was rigid. Someday, someone is going to figure this out and determine the cause and hopefully a method to detect and eliminate it's occurrence.
Until then, marine fish breeders will have to be careful, especially with closed systems, watch for the initial symp-
toms, and always be ready to move a tank of fish to a new,
clean tank.

The V8® rotifer cultures are interesting. I had set up a
tray culture on July 9 with three gallons of new mix saltwater, an innoculum of rotifers, and about an ounce (30 ml) of
V8® juice strained through a 500 micron sieve. This morning, the culture was teaming with rotifers. I didn't make a

count so I don't know how many were produced, but to my experienced eye, production is almost as good as with live algae and a bit better then with a yeast based culture. The flocculent material on the bottom can be siphoned off easier than the heavy, dark green, sheet-like coating that forms on the bottom of yeast based cultures. The culture also harbors a lot of ciliates, apparently a *Euploites* like ciliate and some other very small ciliates or flagellates ?. The V8® culture method may work very well for home based breeders if it does not require too much maintenance. I'll keep working with it and we'll see how practical and effective it may be.

The youngest dottyback larvae are 5 days old today and mortality has been insignificant. They are feeding today on brine shrimp napulii (I didn't forget and leave the air stone out of the culture bottle this morning, perhaps there is still hope for my feeble mind), enriched rotifers, and the remains of the plankton from Monday's collection. I will get plankton again today that should last to next Sunday or Monday. They look good and seem to be growing well. No water change or bottom siphoning has yet been done. Water goes into the tank with the feedings, about 2 cups per day, so demand for water replacement after siphoning is not too great.

The 18 day old larvae are small for 18 days, in one past run the larvae were almost to metamorphosis at this age, and these are still in the mid larval stages. But then they have had only two feedings of wild plankton thus far. The little wild fish larvae is still in this tank and doing well. He has developed 4 bright white pigment spots along the dorsal surface. It will be interesting to see what he becomes.

High tide is at about 7 PM so I will go to get plankton at around 5 PM.

July 12, 1996, 6:00 PM

The plankton tow last night went well. The water looked dark and murky, but the diatom load was not too great and the copepods and other tiny crustacea separated easily from the accumulated diatoms. I can hold a lot of the plankton in a 5 gallon bucket for up to three days and keep many of the copepods alive for feeding. A gentle air release in the bucket keeps the water turning over, allows the diatoms to settle out and keeps the zooplankton active and alive. Of course, a lot does die, especially after 30 hours or so, but it is amazing how much does live.

The 6 day old larvae are really growing well. The tank has a very good larval population, at least 200 at this point. The 19 day old larvae number about 6 or 7. They are larger than the 6 day larvae, but not by much. The lack of wild plankton really stunted their growth. I still can't tell the species of the little wild fish. I hope it isn't piscivorus.

The V8® rotifer cultures are interesting and very productive. The red flocculent material that forms in the cultures can be easily siphoned out after settling, new water replaces that lost to the siphoning, and the culture continues to produce. Harvesting rotifers is easy when the culture is allowed to stand without aeration for a few minutes. The floc settles to the bottom and then the rotifers can be siphoned or decanted. Or, the rotifers can be harvested conventionally, along with a good bit of the floc, and then run through a 250 micron sieve, which passes all of the rotifers and some of the floc. This can also be run through a 150 micron sieve, which retains the very larger rotifers and most of the remaining floc. There are some small bits of floc that get through the 150 sieve and all the smaller rotifers, about 90% of the population, also go though. Many of the rotifers can be reclaimed from the reddish floc that is siphoned out by placing it in a jar and allowing it to settle. The floc sinks to the bottom, the rotifers accumulate in the water column, and they can then be decanted or siphoned off. All the ciliates also go though the 150 sieve. It would be possible to collect only the rotifers over a 70 micron sieve if it were essential to remove the ciliates from the collected rotifers.

It is an interesting population of ciliates, they are about 1/3 the size of a small rotifer and they can be cultured in countless millions on this V8® floc. I'm sure that pure cultures of either rotifers or ciliates can be established, although it might be a bit difficult to make sure that ciliates do not invade the rotifer cultures. So far, one ounce of V8® juice to a 3 gallon tray culture of rotifers, fed every other day, seems to be about right. The culture remains cloudy for almost 24 hours after feeding. A heavily harvested culture, however, may need to be fed every day. It would also be interesting to set up a V8® rotifer culture in a 10 gallon tank. The high volume, deep culture tank would allow greater separation of the floc and the rotifers and make it easier to siphon the floc from the bottom without disturbing the rotifers as much. It would seem, from what I have done so far, that it would be easy to maintain a productive culture over a long period of time using V8® and perhaps some added vitamins and minerals as the culture food.

July 15, 19:96, 11:30 PM

Busy weekend, had guests over the weekend and Joe and Sally are coming to spend the night tonight, Monday. Just bare maintenance over the last few days. Had a hatch on Friday night, 7/12/96. Not a great hatch, only about 100 or so. I still don't know why only a portion of the eggs in the egg ball develop to hatching. I noticed that this time about 30 or so larvae had hatched and then died immediately, before even removal with the siphon. They were floating in the brood stock tank. I got a good look at them through the hand lens and they appeared malformed. The others were strong, however, and I set them up in larval tank B. The pair spawned again on Sunday afternoon, 7/14, and these will hatch on Thursday, 7/18. We are going to Barb's family reunion in Michigan on Friday and will be back on Sunday, but hopefully all will survive if Andrea can come by on Saturday to do a feeding.

All is well with all the larvae. A little mortality but nothing significant. I got plankton this AM, left about 7 AM and I was under the bridge getting plankton before the poor souls that live under the bridge had crawled out from under their cardboard and plastic coverings. Bridges are interesting places in the early morning. The plankton was good, I had to cut it a bit short, but only by 5 minutes, because a rain shower drifted overhead. The plankton was a bit heavy with diatoms, but still separated and concentrated well and there will be enough to feed for the next couple of days. I will get plankton again on Thursday, which should hold the little buggers till the next Monday.

I fed most of the plankton to the large spawn in the 20 gallon tank and a small portion, but enough to keep them fed well, to the new hatch in larval tank B. I was considering feeding this run only the V8® rotifers and brine shrimp, but we will be gone over the next weekend, and the V8® culture was not too strong at this point anyway.

4:15 PM

I sort of let the V8® cultures go over the weekend, although I did feed the yeast based cultures every day. I compared the rotifers from both cultures this morning and the yeast based rotifers were larger, more numerous and more reproductively active than the V8® cultures. The rotifers in the V8® cultures are apparently able to go for long periods without additional feeding since they seem to feed off the floc that forms on the bottom of the culture tray. I went to the health food store today and bought some nutritional yeast and some vitamin B complex tablets and I will add some of these to the V8® cocktail that I will give to this culture every day. Then we will check rotifers again and see how the V8® rotifers compare to the yeast based rotifers.

July 17, 1996, 1:30 PM

Message to myself — YOU'VE GOT WATER RUN-NING IN THE SUMP ON THE 55 GALLON TANK. DON'T FORGET!

There was some overnight mortality in the 20 gallon tank. I counted about 20 dead larvae on the bottom of the tank. The remaining larvae, about 150?, all look good and are feeding well on the remaining wild plankton (very thin by this time, 3 days after collection), enriched rotifers and some brine shrimp napulii. They are 11 days old today. The 5 day old larvae are also looking good. They are feeding well and there are about 40 in the 8 gallon larval rearing tank B. There is another hatch due tomorrow night, 7/12, the night before we leave for Michigan for Barb's family reunion. (Gee, words are interesting. I never thought about how reunion was actually re - union, coming together again, until I had to work at spelling it correctly.)

Anyway, I don't know why there was some mortality in the 20 gallon tank. It isn't unusual to have some mortality in a crowded larval tank, but the orchid dottybacks are so hardy once they are past day 3 or 4, that I seldom see any dead larvae on the bottom. I'll do a bottom siphon and partial water change either this afternoon or tomorrow.

Maybe I better go check that tank, just to make sure that I don't run water all over the floor.—- Got it just right and turned off the water. I was making up for evaporation in both systems by running tap water slowly through a 2" PVC pipe filter filled with activated carbon and into the sump tanks. It takes about 15 to 20 minutes and if one isn't careful, one can wander off, get involved in some other activity and completely forget about the running water. This can really mess up a floor and ruin a perfectly good afternoon.

I am starting a more serious V8® rotifer culture effort. We bought some nutritional yeast and a B vitamin complex tablet at the health food store the other day and so I mixed up a cocktail for the rotifers this morning. I mixed up an ounce of V8® sieved through a 500 micron sieve, one B vitamin complex tablet, a teaspoon of nutritional yeast and couple of drops of Super Selco into about a pint of water. It makes up an attractive bright yellow, reddish brown mix, probably do wonders for me, but I'll feed it to the rotifers instead. I started up a 3 gallon tray culture, seeded it with rotifers from a good yeast based culture, and added about 75 ml of this mixture to the rotifer culture. I will not add any of the bakers yeast, Roti-rich yeast base to this culture and we will see how it does.

The old V8® culture is still doing very well, the mix of ciliates and rotifers has not changed much and I have harvested and used it twice so far. There is not a much V8® in the mix that I fed to the new culture, but then I plan to feed it more often and there is not as many rotifers in the new culture. At this point, I think it is possible to rear all the rotifers necessary for a small home based fish rearing system without culturing algae, but let's give it a month or so of experimentation before coming to any conclusions.

Taped my segment of the TV show, Marine Aquarium World, at the public TV station, WLRN yesterday also. The Miami club is helping the station create a series of 13, half hour shows on setting up and keeping marine aquariums and I did a section for them on culture of marine fish. It seemed to go well, but I think I could have done it better.

July 18, 1996, 6:15 PM

Hurry, Hurry, Hurry, Stress, Stress, Stress.... Tough day, Nothing has gone right, well at least nothing has gone hassle free. Got plankton early this AM, dropped the bucket with the last tow as I was putting into the van, had to do the tow over. Cleaned the bottom of the 20 gallon larval tank, the siphon tube jumped out of the bucket and I put a gallon of water on the floor, set the replacement water up on the tank in a bucket with a siphon down to the tank, the siphon jumped out of the tank and put a gallon of water on the floor, sprayed myself in the face when I washed out the plankton net, the plankton was full of some weird green algae that won't settle out, and on and on. But with luck, I'll have everything done in time to leave on a three day trip early tomorrow morning. Actually I'm thankful for this day even when everything seemed to be an extra hassle. TWA flight 800 went down last night off Long Island with 230 people on board. They don't have any more days of any kind, I can't complain a bit.

I don't have to culture algae any more for the rotifer cultures. The V8® based culture medium seems to work like a charm. I have never seen such healthy, strong, reproductively active rotifers. Almost every rotifer I saw from that culture was carrying eggs, most with three or four eggs and many with 6 to 8 eggs. Harvesting is very easy, I can avoid the floc on the bottom of the culture by siphoning the water from above the bottom with a small siphon and I don't get any of the floc, just a large number of clean, healthy rotifers. It is then easy to condense them down over a 53 micron sieve and either replace the water in the culture or add new water. I can then siphon off the floc and replace that water or decant the water off the floc and return it to the culture if I don't want to make a water change at that time. It is almost as easy to grow rotifers now as it is to hatch brine shrimp.

The egg ball that will hatch tonight has a lot of little eyes in it, it may be a good hatch. I will put it in larval tank B along with the last hatch. There are only about 30, 5 day old larvae in that tank so if the new larvae survive my three day absence, they should have a chance of survival.

Stopped by one aquarium store today to inquire if they would be interested in buying my dottybacks. They were somewhat interested, but not at the regular wholesale price of $20.00. Evidently they import this species themselves and pay only about $12.00 for adult sized fish of this species. So it seems that I could get $10 or $12 for my little friends at this shop. Perhaps I'll check around a bit more next week.

July 22, 1996, 11:30 AM

Hoo Boy, Did you ever feel like you're going up the down escalator at the airport to catch a plane that's leaving in five minutes and you're carrying three suitcases too? Well, I guess that's better than being bored. We left at 6 AM on Friday to visit Barb's sister and brothers in Michigan and returned after midnight on Sunday. Andrea came by once on Saturday morning to feed the fish and the rotifers and now I have to pick up the pieces and get ready for the talk to the Miami club on Tuesday. Lots to do.

All the juveniles and adults came through their three day ordeal beautifully, no mortality. The larvae and the rotifers, however, are a different story. Three days with only one feeding is not an ordeal that young larvae can tolerate. There was considerable mortality in the 20 gallon tank. These larvae are in the mid larval stage now at 16 days old. I counted about 12 dead on the bottom this morning and there were probably more that died on Saturday and Sunday that were gone by today, Monday morning. I would guess that about half the larvae that I had last week are gone. There are still over 50 larvae surviving in the tank so unless there is some latent mortality in the next few days, I will still get a good number through.

The youngest larvae, however, are a total wipe out. No larvae are alive in tank B, that had the little ones that hatched on Thursday night and the 20 or so that were 7 days old last Friday. This tank was absolutely clear this morning, no larvae and no rotifers were left alive in the tank. Only two of the 29 day old larvae are alive in larval tank C, these two are beginning to get their orchid color and will probably metamorphose in a few days. The wild larvae now looks like a mojarra, *Eucinostomus argenteus*?, and is in the post larval stage. I'll keep him a few more days and then probably let him go at the bridge.

The rotifer cultures were almost gone as well. The best cultures after the three days with only one feeding were the 30 gallon outside tank and the inside yeast fed tank. The V8® based tanks still had rotifers but they were very small and starved. I made up a new V8® based food this AM and fed these cultures well. We'll see how they respond. I expect them to rebound very well in the next few days. Even the water in the cultures was clear and was not full of bacteria and ciliates so there should be no problem bringing back the rotifer populations.

July 24, 1996, 10:30 AM

Yesterday was busy. Caught up with a lot of culture chores that were pressing, such as getting plankton, which was pretty good for summer plankton, and getting ready for the next hatch which should be tonight. The egg ball looks very good for a change, lots of little eyes. I cleaned up tank B for this hatch. I think that this may be the last hatch I work with for a while, I've got to get more work done on the books. The mid stage larvae, now day 19, in the 20 are doing very well now that I got a little wild plankton in there with them. There are two, I think, of the 32 day old late larval/early juvenile stage fish left in Tank C. They are either gone, I don't know where they would go, or hiding under the rock that I put in there a few days ago. This is most likely since they tend to hide for a couple of days during the two or three days of final metamorphosis between the larval and juvenile stages.

I gave a presentation, including a video and slides, to the Miami club last night on the *Pseudochromis fridmani* rearing project. It seemed to go well, I think everyone got a kick out of the video. It took a while to get that put together, however.

The rotifer cultures are still depressed. (It's important to keep them happy, so this a major concern.) I rejuvenated the 30 gallon patio culture yesterday, siphoned the gunk off the bottom, removed about 8 gallons and replaced it with the sea water from the plankton collections. This water has been through the 53 micron sieve and I am not trying to maintain an algae culture in the tank so the sea water is not a concern here. I hope that this will bring it back, but if not, it may be time to either clean it up and put the tank away, or restart the culture from scratch. I started two new rotifer cultures in gallon jars, one with an algae (*Nanochloropsis*) base and one with the V8® base. I still have to evaluate the 4 tray cultures and either clean them up and restart them or maintain them if they respond to renewed feeding. The young dottyback pair in brood tank 4 is getting big, the male must be 3 inches now. I saw him last night holed up in the capped off four inch long, 3/4 inch PVC pipe that I put in the tank a week or so ago as a possible den. I recently bought a few 1" PVC caps and I plan to drill about a ½ inch hole in one cap and put two caps on a 4 or 5 inch section of pipe and place this in each tank. I think this setup should make an excellent den with enough room inside for maneuvering around and a small entrance for security, very similar to the natural hole in the rock that the first pair is using.

July 26, 1996, 10:15 AM

Did a lot of fish room work yesterday, cleaned all the tanks and the tank covers. The fish are happy now that all the algae is off the covers and light can get into their tanks. They all had breakfast out on their patios. I should clean the tanks more often. I made up two "dottyback dens" yesterday. I took two 1" caps, put a 4" length of 1" pipe between two caps and drilled a ½" hole in the center of one of the caps. This makes up a nice size den with a relatively small entry hole. I put one of these dens in brood stock tank 1 and 2, tank 4 already had the 5" section of 3/4" pipe with a cap on one end that I had made up long ago for the original pair. The male in tank 4 has already taken up residence in that pipe. The male in both tanks 1 and 2 has explored the entrance to his new den (within 10 minutes of its placement), but I haven't seen either of them enter it yet.

Still haven't sold any of the juveniles to shops. It's hard to sell your babies, and I am not much of a marketeer or salesman either. My idea of selling something is to say, "Gee, you wouldn't want to buy a fish, would you?". I will have to try to move them next week, for sure.

These orchid dottybacks are hardy fish with hardy larvae. There was some mortality in the 20 gallon tank last night, about 12 larvae were on the bottom this morning. I haven't given them as much wild plankton as they need and the rotifer cultures have been depressed, two cultures crashed almost totally after our three day trip with only one feeding during that time. I have had to feed almost exclusively brine shrimp, which is not the best for the mid stage larvae.

I think that shaved shrimp particles may be a possible food at this stage, but I haven't had the time to experiment with preparation and presentation. Despite the much less than optimum conditions that these larvae have experienced during their first 20 days, there are still about 50 of them remaining. I saw one yesterday with a large white "growth" at the middle of the dorsal fin. I was able to capture him and removed him for examination and possible treatment. How do you capture a baby fish? Easy, with a baby food jar.

Actually any small, clear glass or jar will do. You just chase the larval fish with the jar until you get him in a corner or up against the side, and then moving very slowly, position the open jar mouth in front of the larvae and move the jar slowly, very slowly toward the fish. After a few tries the larva swims into the jar, because he can see the rest of the tank through the jar, and then when the jar is turned upright, the fish goes to the bottom of the jar and you can remove the jar and the fish from the tank.

The white growth was actually imbedded into the dorsal musculature of the little fish and looked like a node of dead tissue. I put him in a Petrie dish under the dissecting microscope and could see no parasites, nor any obvious bacterial or fungal growths such as filaments or hyphae, just a node of dead tissue. I put him, all ½ inch of him, into a peanut butter jar with a dose of neomycin and phenicol. He survived for over two hours, so I put a few brine shrimp napulii in the jar also. This morning he was still alive and quite active, but had not fed. The white node seemed unchanged but I knew that he would not survive in the jar much longer so I replaced him in the tank where he would have a fighting chance, despite the danger of the problem spreading to the other larvae. I could have surrounded the jar with black plastic and put a light over it, but I didn't want to put that much effort into it.

I don't know why the 12 larvae died in this tank overnight. I suspect a nutritional problem due to the heavy dependence on brine shrimp and the three days of low food levels. The plankton has also been heavy with algae, road runoff, and organics so there may be a bacterial problem as well. I will get plankton again this afternoon and maybe I'll get most of the survivors through the larval stage. They are already picking up orchid pigment spots and, I expect, because of the larger tank and the wild plankton feedings, that they will be ready to metamorphose at about day 25. I should also do a water change again. They have had only one change of about 5 gallons on day 6 and not much exchange since, just what goes in and out with normal feeding and bottom cleaning. A commercial operation, of course, would be much more demanding of proper conditions, more frequent bottom cleaning, better and more consistent nutrition, water exchange every two or three days and better record keeping. But gee, this is just a hobby project, right?. I've got other things that have to get done too.

I started a new tray culture for rotifers yesterday with 3 gallons of new saltwater, an inoculation of rotifers from the algae based culture and a newly made up V8® based rotifer food. The formulae was about 100 mls of V8®, put through a 500 micron strainer, one B vitamin complex tablet crushed and dissolved and also put through the 500 micron sieve, and about a teaspoon of nutritional yeast (I cut back on the yeast a bit since I think it may stimulate fouling of the culture.) The rotifers really took off and the culture contained many large rotifers, most with multiple eggs this morning. The rotifers really respond to this culture method, but I think it is going to require some careful management, siphoning off the floc on the bottom, removing the rotifers without stirring up the bottom and partial water changes every 3 or 4 days to maintain good quality rotifers. But I also think that with this maintenance schedule, a good producing rotifer culture can be maintained for many weeks. I will continue this culture in this manner and see what happens.

July 27, 1996, 11:00 AM

RATS! RATS! RATS! RATS! Why don't things always go right? Everything would be so much easier if nothing ever went wrong. How could I forget that I was filling the saltwater storage tank? I started filling it with freshwater trickling through the carbon filter, started writing some letters, and totally forgot about the tank. When Barb got home, she asked "Why do I hear water running?" Fortunately the tank had just started to overflow and very little got on the floor, just a gallon or so. But it still took a lot of time to clean up, adjust salinity, and get reorganized.

Then this morning, the latest hatch in larval tank B was almost a complete wipe out. This has never happened before with the orchid dottybacks at day 3, or at any day for that matter. Even under conditions of total starvation, larval fish usually last for 5 days. However, these little dottybacks begin feeding very soon, on the first day and very little yolk is left in the larvae after hatch, and, as I am finding out, they feed very heavily during all the larval stages. I suspect that I did not have enough rotifers in the tank during the first two days and that the larvae did not have the food base to survive until the wild plankton was added. I did not add the wild plankton until the late afternoon of day 2.

The plankton is all still alive in the tank and there are a few larvae left alive, but they seen not to have grown much during their first 2 ½ days. The rotifer populations crashed during our three day Michigan trip since they were fed only once during that time and I fed the dottyback larvae very sparingly after our return because of that. The other possibility is the old toxic tank syndrome, I didn't get the streptomycin into the tank until the afternoon of the first day, but that should have been time enough. This was the tank, however, that had the previous episode of "toxic tank" with the 15 juveniles. I did clean the tank throughly, however, and even washed it out with chlorine after the cleaning. But it's possible that some of the evil bacterium survived. This time I'll add chlorine and let the tank stew in it for a day or so.

I added a good feeding of rotifers this morning so we shall see if the few remaining larvae survive. I also checked the food levels in the tank before adding the rotifers, and although there was a good level of plankton (co-pepods) in the tank, most of them were rather large and there may have been a great lack of food organisms of the proper size in tank. It is easy to look into the tank and see what appears to be a heavy load of food organisms, but upon microscopic examination, find only large organisms, algal cells and detritus. Thus it is very important, especially when using wild plankton, to check the food organism content of the tank microscopically and make sure that the cloud of little dots in the tank actually carries enough of the right sized food organisms.

The pair spawned again yesterday, 7/26/96, and so I will have another hatch to work with next Tuesday. By then the rotifer populations should be back to high levels and I have no trips planned, at least not in the early larval period, so we'll see if the larvae survive this next time.

There was some additional mortality in the 20 gallon tank, about 4 larvae including the one with the node of dead tissue on its back. The rest of them, about 40 or 50, look good and the largest of them are beginning to gain color now at day 21. I put several PVC habitats in the tank and they should soon begin to "hang out" near them.

July 29, 1996, 1:15 PM

I cleaned out larval tank B this morning, wiped it down real good and then gave it super dose of chlorine. It sat for several hours, smelled up the room with a chlorine smell, and turned everything in the tank ghost white. Then I siphoned it clean and wiped it dry. The hatch is tomorrow night and it will be ready. I am also cleaning out larval tank C. I moved the two 36 day old juveniles from that tank this morning to the 20 gallon tank, including their little rock. Many of the 23 day old larvae in the 20 gallon tank have now transformed into juveniles, or are in the process of metamorphosis. The little wild larvae from tank C has indeed become a spotfin mojarra, *Eucinostomus argenteus*, and I moved him to the 55 gallon "grow out" tank. This is indeed a grow out tank, because with all the live rock in it, I'll never be able to get anything out of it once I put it in there. But then I'll cross that bridge when I come to it. Now with two clean larval tanks, I can split the hatch and experiment with feeding regimes, hopefully.

4:30 PM

Just stopped by an aquarium shop with two pairs of *Pseudochromis fridmani*. Each bag had a large, probably male, and a smaller, probably female fish. I really have to sell the stock I have because I have no place else to put juvenile dottybacks. Thankfully, they cohabit well with each other. I have had a problem with only 3 in a tank, but never with a presumed pair, one big and one small, and never with more than 5 in a tank. Anyway, there was only one clerk in the store and he was reading a book. I waited for a while and then he finally looked up with an, "Oh, can I help you?". I explained why I was there, I wanted to sell some tank raised fish. Well, neither the owner nor the manager was there and there wasn't anything he could do. He said they were pretty and he did want to know if they were fresh or saltwater, however. So I left my name and number and he said that they would call if they were interested. I brought them back and put them in the 55 gallon grow out tank. I know I'll not get them out of that tank unless I take out every rock and shake them out of the holes.

I'm just not much of a salesman. I wanted to go to the shops because I figured I could get more for the fish, especially mated pairs, from the shops than the wholesalers, but I don't know if it will be worth the time and trouble. I could give them away, but I hate to give them to the shops and then have them sell them for 40 to 60 dollars.

I should be able to get a little something for them to help with the time and effort of rearing them. I can get $10 or $15 from the wholesalers and it seems that the shops, at least one that I talked to, are only willing to pay collectors prices for them. I know that buying and selling fish is a business with shops and wholesalers, their bottom line demands a "buy low, sell high" policy in dealing with live fish, but if tank raised fish are going to be an important part of the future of the hobby, then breeders should get a little encouragement from the dealers. The hobbyists at the Miami club are very happy with the ones they got at the garage sale and in the raffles at the meetings. They report that they eat anything, are extremely hardy and grow like wildfire, which is also my experience. Well, I'll keep trying, either that or get more tanks going, and I don't have time for that.

July 31, 1996, 1:00 PM

I don't believe that July is over already. I'm not ready for it to be over yet. I haven't gotten everything done yet! And I can't find the reset button on the calender. Oh well, at least everyone else is in the same boat.

A really strong hatch last night. There must be over 600 good strong larvae. The corner of the tank was swimming with them and it was very easy to siphon them out. I put them all in larval tank C and this morning there were so many strong larvae that I set up tank B also and moved about half by dipping a two cup measure into tank C and transferring water and larvae into tank B. I had chlorinated tank B with a about 100 ml of liquid swimming pool chlorine and that's strong stuff, letting it set for about a day and then cleaning out the tank and wiping it down with fresh water and a dechlorinator (sodium thiosulphate).

I observed that the males in both brood stock tanks, 1 and 2, that have the new PVC spawning dens are now occupying their dens at night. The male in tank 2 was even engaging in courtship activity, the "leading dance", trying to entice the female into his den. They are only 4 ½ months old at this point but the male is over 2 inches long already.

I changed out about 5 gallons of water in the 20 gallon tank today. This tank is only about 3/4 full so there are only 15 total working gallons. There was one mortality in that tank today. The water was getting old and it has needed a change for some time. So far in the 24 days that this hatch has been running I have only made two significant water changes. Almost all of the larvae have either completed metamorphosis or are in the midst of it. The larvae in this tank haven't had too much wild plankton, I think I made only about three tows in this period. Most of their nutrition has come from enriched rotifers and brine shrimp napulii, but that ever critical little bit of wild plankton was mixed in there several times.

The tides are favorable early tomorrow AM so I will get plankton at that time. The rotifer cultures are still poor. I cleaned up the oldest yeast culture this AM and started a new V8® based culture. The oldest V8® based culture is still producing good rotifers and I used that one primarily in feeding the new hatch in tanks B and C. With so many larvae in these tanks, I am going to have to scrape the bottom of the rotifer tanks, figuratively speaking, to get enough rotifers to keep them going.

8

August 1996 -
The Great Run!

August 1, 1996, 12:10 PM

Verrry interesting.... With every run, every new observation, one learns. It was a great hatch last Tuesday (7/30), and both larval tanks B and C are loaded with 2 day old larvae. I fed with rotifers yesterday, but checking samples of the tank water under the scope and checking the rotifers collected from the cultures, showed that the levels of actual food organisms in the tanks were marginal. The tanks looked like they had plenty of food but this was deceiving because there were a lot of inert particles in the tanks that gave the appearance of a lot of food, but such was not the case.

I got plankton early this morning, even before the trolls that live under the bridge were up and about. There is a full moon so the current was strong, the tides very high, and the water fairly clear and with a strong load of off-shore plankton. The plankton separated very well, I fed the fraction under 150 microns to the 2 day old larvae and the higher fraction to the 25 day old, now mostly juvenile fish.

(Now I know I shouldn't call the folks that live under the bridge, TROLLS, and I apologize. Most of them are just poor unfortunate souls that are struggling with the demons of addiction or mental illness, or people that can't cope with, nor function in, society as it is now structured. We should help and support them to the extent that it is possible to do so, not reject, demean, and abandon them. A few of them, however, are mean and ugly, and they do live under bridges......)

A check of the smaller plankton fraction revealed a lot of debris, some larger copepods and a fair load of small napulii. I found that I could observe the food organisms in the tank and the larvae with a lesser power magnifying glass than the 10 power loop I was using before. I could

A larval fish's eye view of a fish breeder attempting to see the innermost details of larval fish life.

easily see the individual food organisms and the feeding status of the individual larvae.

It appeared that the tanks were still a bit light on food organisms in the proper size range for the larvae so I added some more rotifers. Examination of the larvae was random but very interesting. Most of the larvae had a gut load of food organisms and were very actively pursuing food. Other larvae were thin and had not been feeding, as their guts were empty. They were most often in a head down, drifting position apparently making no attempt to feed. Perhaps 10% of the larvae were in this condition. I doubt that they will initiate feeding and they will probably die within a day or two. So why do some larvae begin feeding and others do not? Because the food organisms were a bit sparse yesterday? Perhaps, but I doubt that this was the case because there were still enough food organisms to allow every larva to frequently encounter them. Somehow, their feeding response behavior was not switched on. I don't have an answer for this right now. This should be a good run, however, if I can keep water quality up and food levels adequate, I may get many of them though this time.

The rotifer cultures have rebounded well. Rotifer populations in the outside 30 gallon tank culture are increasing rapidly now that I made a 5 gallon water change, removed the detritus on the bottom and am feeding the culture at least once, usually twice a day. The inside tray cultures are also doing well. Tray No. 1, that has had both yeast based and V8® based food is now very strong and the new culture that I started only two days ago and have fed only the V8® based food is also quite strong. Tray 3, an old V8® based culture is still viable and Tray 4, which I haven't checked lately, had a culture of unusual ciliates that I thought might be useful for feeding very small larvae. I don't know how long I can hold this culture, however.

It is obvious after working with *Pseudochromis* for several months, that the most important requirement in rearing these larvae is to provide the proper nutrition. Enriched rotifers to brine shrimp napulii, adequate for clownfish, is not adequate for the orchid dottyback, at least not in my marginal home culture facility. Bill Addison mentioned that they (C-Quest) are able to rear them solely on rotifers and brine shrimp, but they are working with large tanks and, I suspect, have significant copepod levels in the rotifer cultures and in the large, 300 gallon, larval rearing tanks. If so, then these supplemental copepod populations may augment the diet of the larval fish and provide enough essential nutritional factors to increase survival potential. Unlike the *Pomacanthus* angelfish, larval *Pseudochromis* will consume both rotifers and copepod napulii.

The addition of wild plankton into an almost adequate nutritional rearing regime, creates a very hardy larval and juvenile orchid dottyback. Secondly, water quality, primarily control of bacterial toxins is critical. Of lesser importance is traditional water quality concerns; i.e., ammonia, nitrite, nitrate, and dissolved organics; and lighting and physical size and shape of the rearing tank. In other words, with the right food and no bacterial toxins, they can put up with some pretty abysmal conditions and still do very well.

August 3, 1996, 9:30 AM

It is now day three of the "monster" spawn. Things did not go as well as I intended. Mother Nature is always subtly telling you, sometimes not so subtly, that you aren't quite as smart as you think you are. Mortality was very high in this hatch, perhaps around 90%. There are still a lot of larvae alive in the two tanks, but not nearly the large numbers that were there two days ago. Yesterday I noticed, with my magnifying glass, that there were many "DOB" (Dead on Bottom) larvae. The larvae that I had observed not feeding, and evidently some that had initiated feeding, had all died. Why, I wondered, because crowding problems really don't appear until the larvae gain a good bit in size? If 10 or 20 or 40 percent of the larvae can take and survive on rotifers and some wild plankton for at least the first 10 days, then certainly 90 percent of them, baring some congenital problem, could do the same if conditions are adequate.

The most likely answer that I can come up with is lighting. The best success that I have had in rearing these little guys has been in the 10 and 20 gallon tanks that have had a dedicated flourescent light over the tank and these tanks are markedly brighter inside. I used a little mini double flourescent fixture over the 8 gallon larval tanks to do some video taping in some of the other runs and then left it on for the duration of the rearing run when the larvae appeared to do much better with it on. They congregate near the top of the tank and are much more active in feeding. I did not add this small light fixture to either of the two 8 gallon larval tanks, B and C, this time because I had only one of these fixtures and I wanted to keep both tanks under the same conditions.

This morning, noting the continuing mortality and apparent reduced feeding behavior of the larvae, I added the fixture to tank B, the one that apparently had the better survival. The larvae immediately went to the top and displayed strong feeding activity. The larvae in Tank C remained scattered about the tank and did not show the same active feeding as the larvae in Tank B. These tanks are normally lit with one 40 watt flourescent bulb located about 10 inches above the tank. Each of the four tanks is basically exposed to only about 12 inches of this bulb. The light is not bright, but it does light up the tank fairly well and I thought that it would be adequate for the larvae to feed. Evidently not, unless the problem is something else. Anyway, I will experiment a bit more with the lighting factor. We'll see how the two tanks, one with the additional light added at day 3 and one without, do over the next week or so.

The pair spawned again on 8/1, a nice big egg ball. I was going to start letting the spawns go for a while, until I got these books done, maybe a year. I mean, that's what will pay the bills in a few years, not rearing a few hundred fish next month. However, I really want to make a strong run under ideal conditions, good rotifers, good plankton, strong lighting, and good daily care (no trips in the middle of the larval run), just to see what is possible with these orchid dottybacks. So maybe I'll juggle the fish around and free up a tank, or set up the 10 gallon tank again and see if I can do better next time.

I may have found a market for some of my little dottybacks. It is easy to make up pairs when they are juveniles, one larger fish and one smaller fish will turn into a male and female as they mature and putting two together as juveniles becomes a functional pair as they mature. They are tolerant of each other during this period, unlike some other species of dottybacks, and make up good pairs in 10 to 20 gallon tanks. Anyway, the company Oceans, Reefs and Aquariums, has started up in Ft. Pierce on the grounds of Harbor Branch Oceanographic Institution, and they may be interested in purchasing some pairs of orchid dottybacks as an initial brood stock for this species. Jeff Turner will evidently be the distributor for the tank raised fish that ORA produces and he bought 5 pairs of juveniles yesterday.

August 4, 1996, 2:30 PM

Well here it is, a lazy Sunday afternoon, Yeah, right. One who propagates marine fish has no lack of urgent tasks, which can be a blessing or a curse. Most often the latter. Interestingly enough, larval tanks B and C look very much alike, except for the light. The large mass of larvae has, unfortunately, passed on, but there are maybe fifty or so 5 day old larvae in each tank. There may be a few more in the well lighted tank B than in tank C, and although the larvae are more concentrated up under the light in Tank B, there seems to be relatively little difference between the numbers and the condition of the larvae surviving in each tank. Of course, the larvae in both tanks were subjected to low levels of food organisms during the first day or so, the plankton on the tow from 8/1 was not rich in tiny copepods or other small napulii, and I did not get the stronger mini light over Tank B until 8/3, day 4, so these factors may or may not be important in survival. At this point they are all just clues and possibilities.

(As I read this journal over in final edit before laying out the book, I must mention here that one of the important findings during the "Great Run", which is about to begin in this journal, was that it is very important to provide very high levels of enriched rotifers or other small food organisms to the larval orchid dottybacks on the **morning** of the first day after hatch. They are voracious feeders on the first day and do not do well later on if food organisms are not immediately abundant.)

So how many rotifers should one feed to a early larval tank? In terms of numbers, I think 3 to 5 per ml is not too high. When the culture reaches the consistency of apple-sauce, then one has fed too many rotifers, just kidding. It is, however, important to maintain a high level of rotifers in the rearing culture during the entire day. Orchid dotty-back larvae each consume a great many rotifers, and it pos-sible in tanks with a large larval fish population, to feed adequately in the morning and then have few food organ-isms left in the tank at noontime. When the food supply is always low or intermittently low during the the first 5 or 6 days, eventual survival of the larvae is also low.)

I am redoing the 30 gallon brood tank that is on the sys-tem. It was set up with actinic lighting and I had intended to set up a blackcap basslet breeding environment, and I may still do so some day, but right now I need it for some *P. fridmani* grow-out space. I will move the bicolor dotty-back from it into the sump, got to put him someplace, and leave the jawfish in the tank. I doubt that he will disturb the little dottybacks.

August 6, 1996, 10:30 AM

It's always somethin. Technology, any technology is synonymous with hassle. I can imagine Hannibal on top of the Alps screaming "Rats! Rats! Rats! Why can't Fed Ex get that new elephant harness here before Tuesday?" In my case it was the second electronic ballast on one set of flourescent lights on the breeding system to fail in the last few months. I just put that ballast, the second one, on that set of lights only two months ago. Lately, they wouldn't come on in the morning unless I lovingly stroked the bulbs (supplied a ground) and said nice things about them (the magic part of technology). Then yesterday, when my schedule was already very full, they wouldn't come on at all and the ballast remained cool, a bad sign. I tested the bulbs and they were good so it had to be the ballast. I decided to put an ordinary tar filled ballast on those lights, as I did for the other pair of lamps on that rack when the electronic ballast on them also failed a few months ago.

I went to Builders Square and had to chose between two that seemed the same, one for $15 and one for $26. The head of the electrical department assured me that they were the same and the $15 one would work fine. Of course, after installing the $15 dollar ballast, it wouldn't work and by reading the specifications (one of those "when all else fails, read the instructions" things), I found out that the guy didn't know his ballasts after all. It was a 277 volt ballast and not a 120 volt. I had to go out again, this time to Home Depot, found the right one, also at $15, and then install it all again. Hassle, Hassle, Hassle.. Anyway, all is well now, even if I lost half a day and still have to return the wrong ballast.

A good, no, an excellent hatch last night. I had to leave a conference on Fishnet a bit early to catch the hatch just after it happened, but it is a good one. There must be at least a 1000 larvae. Now at last I have a larval rearing run going where everything is as near to optimum as I know how to make it at this point. This is the run I have been hoping to develop for the last six months. The larvae are numerous and strong, I have a good supply of rotifers, the plankton seems to be fairly algae free, I have a better idea of the basic requirements of the larvae, and I don't think I'll be taking any trips for the next 30 days or so. With this run, I should be able to answer a lot of questions that have come up over the last six months. This will also have to be the last rearing run for a while if I'm ever to get any serious writing done this decade.

As mentioned above, I moved out the last hatch from the 20 gallon tank I had set up on the microscope table and put them in the 30 gallon tank that is on the breeding system. There were about 70 juvenile and 12 late or early post larval dottybacks in this tank. These little fish get into every possible tiny little hole or crevice when under the threat of the net. I had made up some little stacks of half inch PVC pipe glued into pyramids and stacks to provide habitat for them as they became juveniles.

One would expect them to hide in the pipes, which they did, and it was easy to simply put the stack of pipes in the net, lift it from the water and slide the little fish into the net. Well, they also got into the very tiny spaces between the glued together pipes, which I found out as I moved the pipe structures by hand to another tank. They also get into the tiniest little holes in the rock and won't come out even when the rock has been out the water for some time. I think a commercial enterprise will have to sell the fish and the rock together.

The difference in behavior between the juveniles and the late larval stages was very evident once they were in the deep 18", 30 gallon tank. The brilliant purple juveniles immediately found holes in the rocks and then positioned themselves just above the rocks darting about the bottom and feeding on the brine shrimp napulii I added to the tank. The pale, pinkish late larval fish stayed high in the water column and did not venture down toward the rocks at the bottom and mid level of the tank. They darted about the top of the tank feeding on the brine shrimp napulii. They are doing very well in this tank now almost two days after the move. The late larval fish must have metamor-

phosed in the last day because they are no longer in the upper water column. They seemed strong and adapted well
to the move and the new tank so I won't consider the alternative. I ordinarily would not have moved them so early,
only 28 days, but I needed that tank for this next run.

I cleared the tank out on Sunday PM, 8/4, scraped the
sides with a stout razor blade to remove algae and barnacles (from the wild plankton), and wiped the tank clean
with a scrubber and fresh water. After letting it dry for a
couple of hours I set it up with new saltwater, added a couple of cups of *Nannochloropsus* algae and set the light back
on the tank. The light was set to run constantly with no
dark period to give the algae a good start.

On Monday afternoon, 8/5, (in between struggling
with ballast replacement) I added rotifers and a dose of
streptomycin sulphate, about 50 mg per gallon. This
would prevent bacterial development in the live tank before addition of the larvae. Monday night I added a few
more rotifers that had been in the enrichment jar, algae
plus Super Selco, for most of the day. Thus the tank was
prepared for the hatch on Monday night, 8/5. Preparing
the tank in this way allows for a growth of algae and a
population of rotifers to develop and give the larvae a
food base for the first day.

The hatch came off Monday night beautifully. There
were at least 1000 larvae crowded up under the light in the
corner of the tank. I had turned off the water flow into the
tank and turned down the air stone previously so the larvae had little flow or currents that might impede their concentration under the flashlight. I siphoned them out into a
gallon jar, it took two gallons and one 4 cup measuring
pitcher to collect them all over a period of about 45 minutes. The first collection, about 20 minutes after first hatch,

was the most dense. The container with the larvae was then placed in the tank and then gently removed releasing the larvae into the rearing tank. The light over the 20 gallon rearing tank was then put back on the timer so that it would be dark during the night and then come on in the morning. It will be maintained on the normal 13 hour photoperiod as are all the other tanks.

This morning at 8 AM the lights came on over the 20 gallon tank and, Hoo Boy, the tank was alive with larvae. There were numerous bubbles on the surface of the tank, probably caused by the Super Selco that gets into the tank with the enriched rotifers, and these bubbles refracted the light into the tank and attracted the larvae. There were great clouds of larvae around the bubbles. I moved the light (a 36 inch, two fluorescent bulb fixture) up a bit, two inches, to lessen light intensity at the surface (this will also reduce the heat put into the tank by the light) and adjusted the air flow to increase the turbulence in the tank. The way the tank (an old homemade tank, 30 x 12 x 12 inches constructed in 1970) is set up, the air release is at the center of the tank so that there are areas of strong turbulence and water flow near the air stream and areas of calm and slow water flow at the ends of the tank. The larvae can move to wherever they are most comfortable with the water conditions in the tank. Interestingly, most, at least 80%, of the larvae choose to be in the area of greatest turbulence. They are extremely active, darting quickly about but always heading into the currents. They are also very tiny, somewhere between 2 and 3 mm.

Unlike some other runs there were no larvae dead on the bottom on the first day. Looking on the bottom from the side to about 4 or 5 inches into the tank with the magnifying glass, I did not see one dead larvae. At 10 AM the larvae were very active and making feeding movements but I could see no food organisms in the guts of the larvae. They had not yet actually ingested food organism despite the active feeding behavior. Now, at 12:10 PM, I can see food organisms in the guts of almost all the larvae I could examine with the glass. You don't have much time to observe the larvae as they swim in the tank, but when one does pause for a moment, and display a lateral aspect, within the range of the glass, one can clearly see whether or not there is food in the gut. So the orchid dottyback larvae must feed on the first day. Many other larvae have a larger yolk sac and usually go through the first day without feeding or at least feed very little. It may be that if the dottybacks do not get a certain minimum amount of food the first day, then they cannot survive even if food is provided in later days.

The dottybacks also have a little different feeding behavior than most other larvae. Other larvae such as clownfish and angelfish display a S shaped posture and a momentary fixation on a particular food organism before a rapid extension out of the S shape, striking at and consuming the food organism. The orchid dottyback just cruises fast, hits the food organism in full motion and keeps on trucking. It looks like a short darting motion rather than a coil and strike. Occasionally the little dottyback appears to have a problem and stops and goes through a violent contortion of head and body and then either spits out the food organism or crams it down into the gut (I can't tell which since it happens very fast and even with the magnifying glass, this is a very tiny happening.) and then swims off.

4:30 PM

I checked the larvae closely right after lunch, even to the point of pulling two of them apart under the dissecting scope to see exactly what they were eating. They were all feeding strongly and the two that I dissected had small rotifers, even some rotifer eggs, in their guts. Because they were feeding so strongly, I decided to get plankton for them today and not wait till tomorrow. I took two 15 minute tows, the last tow was not too strong since the tide was just about high and had almost stopped flowing. I sieved the tows through the 500 micron screen and then sieved half the plankton through the 150 micron screen. I fed the small fraction, less than 150 microns, to the new hatch in the 20 and the larger fraction to the 7 day old larvae in larval tanks B and C. I checked the new larvae with the magnifying glass after feeding the plankton and there was great feeding activity and all the larvae seemed to have full guts.

I think it is very important with this species to provide ample food on the first day. Their yolk sac seems quite small and evidently does not sustain them without feeding on the first day. It could well be that in past runs the sparsity of food on the first and second day doomed most of the larvae because their energy stores were so depleted that they could not recover even when food became more available.

There are still surviving larvae in tanks B and C, but they are not numerous, about 15 in B and perhaps 10 in C. They are now growing well and I should get some though in each tank. The massive mortality on day 3 in these tanks was probably due to sparsity of initial food organisms. I am going to have to scramble to provide enough food for the thousand or so larvae in the 20 gallon tank. Of course, if most of them survive the first few days, I may have big problem in the mid larval stage. A thousand fish is a bit of a load for a 20 gallon tank. I always tell prospective breed-

ers of marine fish never to stock the larval tank with more
than a couple of hundred fish because it is easy to reach a
point where food and space is so limited that none survive
where a hundred or two could well have survived. So do
as I say, not as I do.

Now I have to go and rework the rotifer cultures. The
V8® culture is not doing too well at this point. The yeast
cultures are significantly outproducing the V8® culture. It
has good rotifers, but just not as many as the yeast cultures. Perhaps I need to feed the V8® cultures more frequently and perhaps set up the rotifers in new culture
water more often to keep the V8® cultures in top production mode. More work, but even so, more of a sure thing, a
lot quicker than the algae based cultures, and a lot cleaner
than the totally yeast based cultures.

7:45 PM

Checked the new little larvae just now. They are doing
great. A few dead on the bottom, but only maybe a dozen.
All the larvae have full guts and are very active. A good
first day! Now I better get on line since I promised Joyce
Wilkerson that I would visit her clownfish class on Fishnet
tonight.

August 7, 1996, 11:00 AM

The second day of the **Great Dottyback Run**. So far, so
good. I fed the second half of the plankton tows from yesterday. The second day is never as good as the first day.
There is always some zooplankton mortality, but it wasn't
bad, still a lot of little crustacea alive and kicking. I also fed
rotifers and the little guys are feeding well. I checked the
bottom and there are only a few dead larvae, still only
around 10 or so. Interestingly, the larvae are rather easy to
see for the first half day or so, they look very silvery, like

little slivers of ice. But toward the end of the day and on the second day, they lose that silvery appearance, become more transparent, and blend in with the general color of the tank so well that you have to look very close to see them. A close look, however, reveals myriad little larvae tirelessly darting in the turbulence around the top of the air stream. I looked at the guts with the glass and although some were still with empty or near empty guts, most had begun to pack themselves with rotifers and plankters.

The inside rotifer cultures are doing well. The yeast cultures have very heavy populations and the V8® culture was quite sparse. I reestablished the V8® culture with new water and new rotifers. I will take better care of it this time and see if I can keep it at high production. I did not add yeast to it this time and I did not strain the V8® before making up the feeding solution. I did add a bit of Super Selco and the vitamin B. After collection from the yeast and\or V8® cultures, I concentrate the rotifers on top of the 53 micron sieve (taking care not to expose them to air), put them in new saltwater and add some algae and a couple of drops of Super Selco. Then I have about 2 to 4 cups of this rotifer stew and I leave it with very light aeration for 2 to 6 hours before feeding. Usually I feed part of it after about two hours and the rest at various times during the day.

August 8, 1996, 10:30 AM

Day 3 of the Great Run!

I checked mortality on the bottom this AM and found only a few dead larvae here and there on the bottom. The great majority, one heck of a lot of larvae, are still in the turbulence areas at the top of the tank, darting about actively and feeding on the rotifers that pass by. The plankton that was added to the tank so far has only been that fraction of the tows that passed through the 150 micron sieve. This is not an abundant fraction and there is very little plankton left in the tank at this time. The food of the larvae is almost exclusively enriched rotifers. I did feed a bit of new hatch brine shrimp napulii late yesterday afternoon (the second day) and observed many of the larvae with orange guts. I will get plankton again today, weather permitting, and see how the larvae respond to the additional plankton feedings. I have not yet siphoned the bottom of the tank or provided a water change. The water that enters the tank with the food increased the volume in the tank by about 10% over the first 3 or 4 days.

The last large hatch of dottybacks that I worked with, now at day 9 in larval tanks B and C, had extensive mortality on day 3 in the AM. In fact almost a total wipe out. Today at day 9 this hatch has about 15 survivors in tank B and only two or three in tank C. The main observable difference in the two tanks, aside from the chlorination of tank B before the hatch, contrasted with the fresh water wipe down of tank C, is the intense light from the two bulb mini light that has been over tank B. The main difference between the current 3 day old run and the last run has been the attention to feeding in the first day, the strong effort to provide a good and abundant food base in the first few days of the run.

The V8® culture is doing very well. I doubled the amount of V8® culture food that I have been using and the rotifers are abundant and full of eggs. This is a very viable method of rearing abundant rotifers but it takes daily husbandry, as does everything else in this hobby. I'm not sure how nutritionally complete the rotifers are that are reared with the V8® method, but I don't see how they can be any worse then those reared with the yeast base culture. The algae method, I'm sure, produces the best rotifers for culture, but the V8® method is less hassle and less technically demanding.

8:50 PM

The third day of the Great Run is over. There are a few mortalities scattered on the bottom, but very few. I also observed a few drifting larvae with empty guts so I expect a few more mortalities in the morning. The plankton tow went very well, two hours before high tide and the current was strong, the water clear with little algae and the zooplankton was fair, not very heavy. The larvae are also feeding on a little brine shrimp, not too much however. I think a little brine shrimp may provide needed energy at this point, and as long as plankton is available also, it shouldn't do too much damage to the larval livers. Because of the heavy load of larvae in the tank, which will remain so I hope, I will have to do more extensive water changes during the mid and late larvae stages, especially if I experiment with feeding tiny shrimp particles.

I talked with Dr. Dave Vaughn from Harbor Branch today and I think that they will take about 30 of the juveniles next week. Which is good, because I am going to need that tank space.

August 9, 1996, 11:00 AM

Day 4 of the Great Run! As expected, there is some mortality evidenced by a scattering of larvae on the bottom, in my estimate, probably no more than 50 dead larvae. It is, however, very light relative to the total number of larvae in the tank. I would estimate that there has been no more than 5% mortality so far and quite likely, less than that. They are feeding very actively, as would be expected. They are now ranging more throughout the tank rather than concentrating in the more turbulent areas near the surface. Many still remain in these areas, however. Some of the larvae are feeding heavily on brine shrimp napulii (I add a few brine shrimp to the tank each day but very few), others are apparently feeding heavily just on rotifers and/or plankton, others are feeding very lightly, and a few do not seem to be feeding at all. The numbers of those not feeding, however, seem to be decreasing markedly.

I may do a water change, maybe 10 to 15%, and bottom siphon tomorrow or Sunday. I'll do it late in the day, or early before feeding to avoid loss of food organisms. It is easy to pick up larvae when they are so small, so I have to use a small bore siphon, rigid air tubing for the siphon stick and air tubing for the hose. It is slow, but it gives the larvae some protection from capture.

I wouldn't be surprised if most marine fish species that produce large numbers of pelagic larvae have a genetic mechanism that provides the larvae with differential survival characteristics. Some larvae from the same spawn seem adapted to survive for a long time in the plankton, feeding relatively lightly, and others seem adapted to take advantage of high concentrations of food, feed very heavily, and grow quickly. The light feeders may be more adapted for survival under conditions of low food and be able to make long larval journeys to colonize far off areas, whereas others may survive more readily when food is very available and rapid growth will enable them to colonize areas nearer to the adult population that produced the spawn. This is just a musing prompted by long term observations on the great differential survival and growth of the larvae of a variety of species when maintained under the same conditions of food, light, and chemical environment in the same larvae rearing tanks.

I fed about a quarter of the remaining plankton, will probably feed the remainder late this afternoon or tomorrow morning. I also added rotifers enriched with Super Selco and algae (*Nanochloropsus*) and added a cup of the algae to the rearing tank to provide the rotifers already in the lion's den, er, the rearing tank, with some sustenance — to better prepare them for incorporation into a larval dottyback.

The V8® culture rotifers are looking good, but their abundance is below that of the yeast based culture. I think the problem is that the food base in the V8® cultures does not remain suspended as long as the yeast, thus the V8® cultures require twice a day or perhaps three times a day feedings rather than the once a day feeding that the yeast cultures can tolerate. I will step up the feeding schedule on the V8® cultures and see if this picks up rotifer production. The individual rotifers look good, however, normal size and color, and eggs are present on most individuals.

There are about 10, ten day old larvae remaining from the hatch of 7/30. These 10 are in larval tank B and are looking good. They feed on plankton, rotifers and some brine shrimp. I would expect all 10 or so to survive into juveniles at this point. The pair spawned again last Wednesday, 8/7, a nice big egg ball. They have settled into a routine of spawning every six days, two days after the last hatch. How can I let a 1000 larvae go down the drain? After this last run, I don't need to keep rearing them except to fine tune the techniques and I don't have the tank room or the time to keep going, besides, Barb is beginning to look foreboding when she says that we are going to have to sell the house if I don't get some more books done. But it would be neat to try a big run in that 30 gallon tank that is already plumbed into the rearing system..... I wonder if there is a marine fish breeders anonymous?

5:15 PM

The fourth day is winding down and the great run is still cranking along. Many, if not most are feeding on brine shrimp napulii. I will cut back on the BS over the next few days, feed more rotifers, since I am afraid of the effect of feeding too much brine shrimp. I still have a quarter of the last plankton tow, which is losing value every day as the zooplankters die off. I will get plankton on Sunday or Monday, as the opportunity presents. If I start to get mortality, of course, I'll get plankton sooner.

August 10, 1996, 11:00 AM

Day 5 of the Great Run! Looking good! Mortality is still insignificant. The larvae are feeding on the last of the plankton and, mostly, on enriched rotifers. They are spread throughout the tank and swim vigorously all over. It is still very hard to see them since they blend in so well with the general tank color.

I think lighting, and water quality, especially control of bacterial toxins is very important, but the exceptional survival on day five of this run has really brought home the overriding importance, particularly with this species, of having enough food organisms with the right nutritional base during the first few days of the rearing run. Other runs, when providing ample food organisms on the first day was not considered essential, had great mortality on the third day, despite addition of ample food organisms on the second and third day.

There have been no water changes and no bottom cleaning yet on this run. The only water change has been the relatively small amount of water added with the addition of food organisms. The result has been a very slight dilution of the original culture water in the tank. I will make a water change of about 5 gallons, approximately one third of the tank, this evening or tomorrow AM. I ran water quality tests on the tank today just to see what the larvae have been subjected to so far.

PH Coralife pH pen... 8.0
Sea Chem chemical pH test...8.0

Sea Chem NO_2..... 0.2
Sea Chem NO_3..... 1.6

Sea Chem free ammonia   0.0
Sea Chem total ammonia   0.15

Salinity.... Aquarium Systems full range S.G. meter.. 1.026 (36 ppt)

Salinity is a bit high but a range of salinity from 32 to 38 ppt does not seem to affect survival, at least on the basis of empirical observations. Actually I really don't worry too much about the typical water quality parameters since ammonia is usually in the less toxic ionized state at the usual pH of marine systems; and nitrite and nitrate do not seem to bother fish larvae too much, especially nitrate; and pH is typically 7.9 to 8.1. Water changes every few days usually maintain water quality within the rather broad areas that are required for fish culture. Coral culture, on the other hand, requires great attention to the chemical and physical environment.

Well, the grand kids are over today so I have to go get busy with them.

August 11, 1996, 11:30 AM

Day 6 of the great run! and the little larvae are still as abundant as flies on a cow pie. I siphoned their little bottom this morning and removed about 4 gallons, roughly 25% of the water. I am replacing that now with a slow drip of synthetic sea water. I have used a variety of artificial sea salts, Coralife, Instant Ocean, and Sea Chem, and some natural seawater in the rearing runs over the last 8 or 9 months with no noticeable difference in success or failure of the runs. Other factors, such as food and feeding, primarily, and perhaps the streptomycin addition, and lighting, seem to have more effect on the success of the runs than the type of saltwater. I will also add about 25 mg/gallon streptomycin sulphate to this run to make up for the water change and provide a secondary dose for the remainder of the run.

This basic rearing technique works well, at least for the orchid dottyback, as evidenced by the exceptional survival I have had with this run in a 20 gallon tank. There must be close to 500 six day old larvae in this tank at this point. There is a great need, however, for more research into the actual need for streptomycin. I have not made runs without it since the runs began to be successful and produce juveniles, and if it is necessary for survival of the larvae, determination of the optimum dosage and time of applications. There is also much to be done on the larval diet, what can be used to substitute for the wild plankton, whether careful feeding of properly enriched rotifers, brine shrimp and grated shrimp micro particles can bring them through in large numbers and if so, what is the precise technique that is required? I have been successful with a small scale culture project with *P. fridmani* but there is still much to do and I don't have the time or facilities to do so. Well, at least this is a good start.

I used my little homemade siphon to clean off the detritus on the tank bottom. It consists of a short piece of half inch CPVC pipe (it's a bit smaller in diameter than regular PVC pipe), about 2 inches long with a saw cut along the length off center and at an angle which provides a sort of cutting edge that scrapes the bottom. The ends are closed off and a 14 inch section of rigid air tubing extends from a hole in the top center of this tube to the 5 feet of air tubing that is the siphon tube. It works real well to clean the bottom and remove water for a water change without picking up the larval fish. I didn't get a one in the four gallons or so that were removed. I'll make up a diagram of this device for the breeding book.

The V8® culture produces rotifers just as well as the yeast based cultures for the first five or six days, but then it seems to break down and although many rotifers are present in the culture, they are not as abundant as in yeast cultures of the same age. More experimentation needs to be done here as well. I wonder how instant mashed potatoes or corn starch would work as a basis for a rotifer culture? Hmmmm...

2:30 PM

Interesting, I enriched the rotifers this morning with algae (*Nanochloropsus*) and Super Selco, as usual, but I also added a little bit of the V8® culture base because the algae was a little thin. So far today enriched rotifers has been the only food organisms fed to the larvae. The larval guts have a distinctly reddish hue, not the bright orange that is apparent when brine shrimp napulii are fed, and not the white or gray hue when plankton and/or the usual rotifers are fed, but a distinct pink to red shade that must come from the V8® culture base. I don't know if this is bad or good, or indifferent at this point, but the larvae are so numerous and so active, and so well fed that I don't think it could be a negative. I will put off the plankton tow until tomorrow since they seem to be doing so well. I would love to try to go the rest of the way without plankton, but I think it is more important at this point to bring through as many as possible with all the techniques available to me to establish a baseline understanding of what can be done with limited facilities.

I also observed one or two unhatched brine shrimp cysts in the guts of larvae. These were cysts from the brine shrimp feeding of late yesterday. Sometimes this can be a big problem in feeding larval fish since the cysts can cause intestinal blocks and kill the larvae. The larvae can usually pass the cysts, though, and be none the worse for it. The magnifying glass up against the side of the aquarium allows very good observation of the larvae, even to the point of identification of gut contents. The real significance of this observation, however, is that if the larvae can take an inanimate particle, then it may be possible to feed tiny particles of raw or cooked shrimp in the late larvae stage and avoid or at least greatly limit the amount of brine shrimp napulii in the larval diet.

The current spawn is due to hatch tonight. I haven't prepared a tank for them. I think that rather than dilute my efforts and available food supplies, I will let them go or drop them in larval tank C, which has only one or two stunted larvae from the previous hatch. The important thing now is to follow though on the great run in the 20 gallon tank!

10:30 PM

Hoo Boy... A great hatch tonight. There must be 800 to a 1000 orchid dottyback larvae that hatched into the brood stock tank just now. Unfortunately, there is not much that I can do with them. I don't have the rotifers, tank space or time to work with another hatch at this point. I siphoned them into the old larval tank C, where all the larvae from the hatch just before the Great Run died out. If I have some extra rotifers and plankton, I'll toss it in there, but I'm going to have to learn to let these extra hatches become part of the food chain.

August 12, 1996, 9:30 AM

Day 7 of the Great Run! No significant mortality so far. There was little food in the tank this morning, the water was very clear and hundreds of transparent little orchid dottybacks are darting about the tank. A few minor problems, only one RATS! exclamation warranted. The tides are in the absolute worst possible configuration. High tide is at 7 in the morning and 8 at night. This means that I have to get plankton at 5 or 6 AM or 6 or 7 in the PM, neither of which is a decent time. So I went this morning but made it bit late and didn't hit the optimum flow. Another small rip appeared in Julian's plankton net also, just a little one and Barb can patch it up easily. I'll have to give it back to Julian when it gets all ripped up and then buy a new one. Just Kidding.

The plankton was good, however, no algae or diatom blooms, and I did get enough to give the larvae a good feeding of wild plankton, which should give them a good mid larval stage boost. They are growing very well, about a quarter inch in total length at this point. All seem to be feeding well and there are few, if any, drifters (A drifter is a larva that has stopped feeding, gets thin and drifts in a head down aspect for a while before dying.)

1:15 PM

I just went through the rotifer cultures. Problems. Only one culture, the oldest yeast based culture is still good. The other three, one V8® and two yeast cultures, were full of ciliates and had very few rotifers. I think I know why, however. Being frugal, I used the water from the plankton tows for these rotifer cultures. Bad move. Although most plankters are retained above the 53 micron sieve, the really small stuff, such as ciliates and flagellates and a few other things, go through and evidently bloom along with the rotifers at first, so there is a bloom of rotifers and ciliates in the first four to 6 days, and then the ciliates take over. I don't think that they feed on the rotifers, although that is a possibility, but as their populations explode, I think they out-compete the rotifers for the available food.

The plankton water can be used for rotifer culture or even in the breeding/rearing system, but to be safe it must be sterilized with chlorine and then dechlorinated before use. This requires extra time and use of additional containers to hold and treat the water and may or may not be worth the effort.

I did set up the three cultures once again, this time with artificial sea water, and seeded them with well washed rotifers from the good culture, so this will be a better test of the suitability of the V8® culture base. Both the yeast culture and the V8® culture were started with the same water and the same rotifer seed divided in half, so all factors are the same this time: the amount and source of the culture water, the rotifer seed, and the time of the start of the culture.

August 13, 1996, 11:30 AM

Day 8 of the Great Run! Still no mortality! There are
hundreds of these little 8 day old, quarter inch long orchid
dottybacks in the tank. They are transparent except for the
gut and the eyes and two rather bright pigment spots on
the dorsal and ventral aspect of the caudal peduncle. The
guts were mostly empty at first light, but now they all
have a full, white gut. They tend to group up in two
places. Each end of the tank about equidistance from the
air stone has a small cloud of larval fish. They are in constant motion in the currents, some come up against the
glass and appear to pick rotifers off the side. A few rotifers
are always on the sides of the tank, apparently eating the
algae or microorganisms attached to the glass, and the larval fish grab the rotifers and then shake a bit as they apparently ingest the rotifer.

There is still some zooplankton from yesterdays feeding. The copepods tend to group near the surface in the
bright light and form a swarm in a small area. Many larvae
dart through the swarm apparently capturing small copepods and other zooplankters. I will feed mostly the enriched rotifers today, perhaps a few new hatch brine
shrimp late this afternoon. Tomorrow I'll get plankton
again in the AM.

1:30 PM

Interesting... I looked at the larvae carefully through
the magnifying glass and saw many with empty guts, the
rotifer population in the tank was sparse, they are eating a
lot of rotifers now. I added rotifers to the tank and a small
amount of brine shrimp napulii. I am trying to go as
lightly as possible with the brine shrimp. I did see a few
larvae with brine shrimp cysts in the gut and one larva
had at lease five of these cysts lined up one after the other

in its gut. I don't know if he can survive this or not. Even if the cysts pass out and do not obstruct the gut, he may suffer starvation since the cysts carry no food value.

Decapsulated cysts would be an advantage, but relatively few cysts pass though the separation process and it does not appear to be a significant problem, at least not with this run. This does tell me, however, that dottyback larvae this small, and probably other larvae as well, certainly clownfish larvae for I have seen them take cysts also, will accept particulate, non active food and it may be possible to rear them on grated shrimp particles, although upkeep of the tank will be a bear, although maybe not too bad with small tanks...

August 14, 1996, 11:15 AM

Day 9 of the Great Run! And there is some mortality. I saw about 3 or 4 dead larvae, which means that there are probably 8 or 10 altogether hidden on the bottom. There are also a few drifters that have stopped feeding for some reason, so I expect some more light mortality in the days ahead. The tank was almost empty of food organisms this morning. Yumpin Yimminy, they eat a lot. (Yumpin Yimminy is a mild expression of surprise, I don't know where I got that from but I suspect it was from my Norwegian born father.)

I went out at 7 AM and got plankton on the incoming tide. It was reasonably good plankton, the water was clear and clean and flowing fairly strongly, no algae blooms. The zooplankton was a bit sparse, however, and I took two 45 minute tows. I separated it above and below 250 microns instead of the 150 because the larvae are much larger now. They started feeding immediately upon introduction of the plankton at about 9:30 AM. Examination of the larvae and food levels in the tank with the magnifying glass indicated that there was not enough food organisms of the proper size in the tank and some of the larvae were not feeding as they should. I collected rotifers to supplement the plankton, and fed some, but most of the collection is now under enrichment and I will feed part of it about 1 PM and the rest about 4 or 5 PM.

There is great disparity in the size of food organisms that individual larvae will accept. All of them will accept rotifers easily and some have no problem feeding on brine shrimp. The plankton is all sizes and most larvae can find something in that offering that suits them. There seems to be a gap in between rotifers and brine shrimp napulii that some larvae cannot bridge without the intermediate step of wild plankton. I still think serious nutritional problems develop when the larvae are given nothing but, or almost nothing but brine shrimp napulii from day 6 or 8 through day 16. (Actually, they die on about day 16 of this nutritional regime.)

I can't get enough wild plankton to feed it exclusively during the larval period. I think they could easily be brought through on just wild plankton, but this would entail two or more tows per day for a large hatch, which just isn't feasible for me at this point, especially since it is a round trip of 40 miles to the bridge. Fortunately, the larvae seem to do fine with a main diet of enriched rotifers and sparse brine shrimp feedings along with some wild plankton. I think that feeding raw or slightly cooked tiny particles of shrimp will also fit into a successful diet, but I'll experiment with this a bit later. Cooking would bind, or "fix", the protein and reduce tank fouling, but acceptance by the larvae may be compromised.

I am starting to have to scrape a bit to get enough rotifers. The outside tank is still producing but not abundantly and the inside cultures are coming up, but except for one tray, they are not yet harvestable. The ciliate infestation cost me two good rotifer cultures. Now I use chlorine to treat the natural seawater that comes in with the plankton tows if I want to use it for food culture. I am experimenting with instant mashed potato mix for rearing rotifers. It shows some promise, at least the rotifers have not died and are with eggs after one day. There may be other substances that may work well, such as corn starch, either by themselves or with V8® juice. I'll have to take a good look around the supermarket. I don't think a processed food, yeast, V8®, corn starch, potatoes or anything else will rival algae cultures in production of clean, abundant, healthy rotifers, but the right mix may provide an adequate substitute for algae if the cultures are properly maintained.

4:30 PM

It is now difficult to keep enough food in the tank. They went through the plankton in a few hours, went through the days collection of rotifers in another couple of hours and now they are starting to scarf up new hatch brine shrimp. I hope the new hatch brine shrimp brings them through the next week or so as a supplement to wild plankton since they seem to be "outgrowing" rotifers. I think I will try the particulate shrimp, maybe this afternoon. I may have to change water afterwards, unless I can flush the particles well enough.

5:45 PM

Well, I tried the shrimp particle technique with the 9 day old larvae in the twenty gallon tank. First I ran the grated shrimp through a 250 micron sieve and washed it over the 53 micron screen. The result was some very, very fine particles, about one forth the size of new hatch brine shrimp and smaller. I fed this and there was a lot of activity on the part of the larvae, swimming into and through the particle cloud. I don't know if any of the larvae fed on the particles. Then I tried the same thing only with the 500 micron stainless steel sieve. The particles were considerably larger, the size of new hatch brine shrimp and smaller.

The larvae seemed to show interest in these particles, but again I could not confirm actual feeding on the particles. I did observe several larvae with brine shrimp cysts in the gut so I know that they will take inanimate particles. Many of the larvae have white guts, which may be from the shrimp particles, but may also be from the plankton and rotifers as well. I think I will try feeding shrimp particles again in the morning when there is not so much food in the tank and I may be able to get a better look at the larval feeding activity.

I think the next few days are going to be critical, although it seems that every day is critical in some way. The transition from rotifers to larger food organisms or particles seems to be easily made by some larvae while others either have difficulty or don't make the switch at all even though all foods are available. I hope there won't be too much mortality and I have to be careful not to overfeed on brine shrimp napulii.

August 15, 1996, 11:30 AM

Day 10 of the Great Run! Interesting morning, but then almost all mornings are interesting. There was some mortality last night, I saw maybe a dozen dead larvae, but all the rest, all 500 or more were swimming about and almost all had very little food in their gut. (Actually I don't really know how many there are in that little tank. I used to be

Preparation of "shrimp bits" for late larvae and early juveniles. The frozen shrimp ball is lightly grated and the particulate shrimp is forced through the 500 micron, stainless steel mesh strainer. The shrimp particles are kept in ice cold water at all times.

able to look at tank full of late larval or juvenile clownfish and estimate the number to within 25 to 50 fish, but you have to stay in practice to do this. The orchid dottybacks move relatively fast and the mass of larvae keeps changing position and shape so it is not possible to try to break them up mentally into groups of small numbers and then add them up. 500, however, seems like a reasonable estimate.)

I worked with the shrimp particles a good bit this morning when there wasn't much other food in the tank and I could better see if the larvae were taking them. I first grated the frozen shrimp with the fine grater and then put it through the 500 micron sieve and washed it over the 53 micron sieve. The resulting particles were a little big and the larvae seemed very interested but they did not seem to be taking the large particles. I then put it through the 250 micron sieve and the particles seem a bit too small, although the larvae were very active and were attracted to, and swam through the cloud of particles.

I also took some of the larger particles, cooked them for 30 seconds in the microwave and put them back through the 500 micron sieve. The cooked particles were much whiter and more discrete in shape and form. I could see some larvae actually taking the particles and the general color of the guts of the larvae became more whitish. I think this technique has promise, especially for older larvae, maybe from day 15 on through the juvenile stage. I guess the worse thing about the shrimp particle feed is that it tends to foul the water despite washing the shrimp water off the particles before feeding them. I will have to siphon the bottom of the tank this afternoon and change a good 5 gallons of the water.

I also fed the shrimp particles to the 16 day old larvae in larval Tank B. There was much more food in this tank from the day before since there is only about 6 larvae remaining in this tank, but they did seem to take the particles more readily. I fed the remaining plankton to both tanks and then later some enriched rotifers. The rotifers seem to be a bit small for the larvae at this point. I'll also add a bit of new hatch brine later, but still being careful not to feed too much.

5:00 PM

I changed about 8 gallons of water this afternoon and siphoned the bottom of the tank. The change was really needed after feeding the shrimp particles. I also added a bit of streptomycin and a little neomycin, about 30 mg/gal of new water of each antibiotic. I think I will do this as insurance at each water change. I don't think it will hurt the larvae and it may make a very great difference in survival.

August 16, 1996, 2:20 PM

Day 11 of the Great Run! This "great run" has taken over my life. All day long, it's "are they eating?, what are they eating?, any mortalities?, does the water need changing?, the bottom siphoning?, what are the tides?, when will be the best time for plankton?", and on and on it goes. I'm not complaining though, it is intriguing and I'm learning a lot, but I'm also glad that I won't be doing this all the time.

They are looking good, still. A little more mortality, about a dozen today. I got plankton first thing and it was pretty good. No algae and a fair load of zooplankton. They really chowed down when the plankton was introduced into the tank. I put in the fraction below 250 microns, and a little bit of the above 250 fraction just in case a few of them were ambitious today. I also tried, a little later, some commercial pelleted fish food that I had ground up in a mortar and pestle to a size just a bit larger than a rotifer. They seemed to take this quite well, although it is hard to tell for sure, and I will try this again first thing in the morning when the guts are empty. Even if they take it well, I'm not sure how easily they will be able to digest it. If it does work well, however, it will be better than the shrimp particles because it will not foul the tank as much.

I really have to scramble to keep this many larvae with enough food. I think that one of the problems in the past was not realizing just how much food a large number of larvae require, especially during the first week. They can clear that tank of food organisms in a few hours. Also they produce a lot of fecal pellets that drift in the water for a while and look like food organisms from a distance. That and other detritus can make a tank look as if it is full of food when the actual density of food organisms is quite low. Examination of a sample of the water under the dissecting scope or looking at the larvae and the food organisms in the tank through a magnifying glass can quickly reveal the true nature of the food load in the tank.

More troubles with the rotifer cultures. I keep getting a sort of algae or fungus (tiny white filaments) along with ciliates that keep the rotifer populations depressed. I started up a good algae based culture that I can use as a seed to begin other cultures again from scratch. Thank goodness that the Great Run is at about the end of it's dependence on rotifers.

August 17, 1996, 11:10 PM

Day 12 of the Great Run! Very little mortality, perhaps 6 to 10 per day have died over the last two or three days. The tank is still alive with little transparent dottybacks. They are about a quarter to three eighths inch long (5 to 10 mm). This is a very rough measurement, I hold a rule up to the side of the tank and try to get an estimate of length as a larva swims by, sort of like trying to guess a sprinter's shoe size during the 100 meter sprint. I fed finely ground dry fish food first thing this morning. They did take it, especially the larger larvae. This is a very good sign for it may make them easier to rear with less dependence on wild plankton.

There is so much nitty gritty research to be done on the diet and feeding of marine fish larvae. The orchid dottyback is a very good subject for such research. They are more difficult then clownfish to rear, yet they are very hardy in many ways once bacterial toxins are under control and the basic nutritional requirements (whatever they are) have been supplied. They also spawn frequently, if my pair is typical, every 6 days; produce a large number of larvae, at least 600 per spawn, perhaps more; the adults can be maintained in a reasonable size tank, perhaps 10 and certainly 20 gallons; they grow very fast, salable size within 3 to 4 months; and they are fairly valuable on the marine life market.

Anyway, this run, now halfway through the shortest normal larval period, is still doing very well, and if I can keep them fed properly and the water reasonably clean, which in a 20 gallon tank shouldn't be too hard, I should get a goodly number through.

I fed the larvae the rest of the plankton after the experimental feeding of the finely particulate dry food, which was, by the way, already soaked in fresh water and fed by eye dropper to various parts of the tank. They will get enriched rotifers at about 1:00 PM, along with some brine shrimp late in the afternoon. I will get plankton again either tomorrow or on Monday PM.

The larvae in the 8 gallon larval tank B are still 6 in number and are doing well now on day 18. I don't pay a lot of attention to them these days since I am so wrapped up with the larvae in the 20 gallon tank, feeding them the leftovers and checking on them only once or twice a day. They don't seem to mind, however, they seem to understand my obsession with their younger brethren, and they are growing well.

I cleaned off the glass on the 55 that is filled with rock and houses 14 of the juvenile orchid dottybacks. It is really amazing how much better you can see into a tank after the inside glass has been cleaned! All 14 of the little guys are still there, except that they are not little guys anymore. A few of them are or have evidently become males and they are nearly adult size now. They are almost 5 months old. The vivid magenta color of these fish is truly spectacular!

The yeast based rotifer cultures have crashed, evidently a lot of ciliates and those nasty little white filaments, but the V8® cultures have done well. One of the big problems with the V8® base is that the tiny vegetable particles drop out of solution relatively rapidly, a few hours. I mixed a little corn starch with the V8®, and also a little finely ground instant mashed potatoes with the juice and B vitamin mix on the theory that the fine carbohydrate particles may pick up some of the vegetable matter and carry it into the rotifers as well as remain in solution for a longer time. It seems to be working so far in that the rotifers from this culture are strong and have many eggs.

The larvae require so much food now that it would be very difficult to maintain them with just wild plankton. Both rotifers and brine shrimp napulii are required just to supply the amount of food that they require. I have been using brine shrimp napulii when necessary, but I have been using them sort of as a food of last resort. When there is no more wild plankton, and I have used up the rotifer cultures for the day, and the larvae have empty guts and are looking for food, then I add a little brine shrimp. They can clear the tank of food in an hour or so and have empty guts within a couple of hours after feeding.

August 18, 1996, 3:00 PM

Day 13 of the Great Run! No significant mortality. They have grown noticeably in the last day or two. Some seem to be pushing a half inch in length. The guts were empty this morning, as was expected, and the tank was bare of food. I tried some finely ground flake food and they showed great interest, but I could not really affirm that they ingested any substantial amount of the particles.

I collected plankton and it was excellent this morning. The tide was running rapidly and pushed a lot of water though the net. The plankton was full of copepods and there were more copepods in the fraction above 250 microns than I could use. The larvae are stuffed. Their little stomachs are as round and full as little footballs. I don't think I will have to feed any rotifers or brine shrimp today at all, but we will see how they are later this afternoon.

9:00 PM

Boy, do those guys eat! I changed about 3 gallons of water late in the day and replaced the streptomycin that was removed with the old water. I added the last of this day's aliquot of plankton and they pigged out again. Now, a few hours later, there is little food in the tank and little food in their guts, but the light is scheduled to go out in a few minutes so they will have to go to bed with an empty stomach. I will feed the other half of the plankton tomorrow morning and then go back to rotifers and brine shrimp for the rest of the day.

I can see how, with limited food, it would be very easy to try to rear too many larvae, not have enough food for all of them and not realize this, and thus not be able to rear any through the juvenile stage and not know why. It's very important not to try to rear more larval fish than there is food available.

August 19, 1996, 1:00 PM

Day 14 of the Great Run! Still looking good. There were five mortalities on the bottom this morning. A couple of these were larger fish, which is a little troubling since the mortalities are usually smaller fish. However, all the rest seem quite active and healthy. Some mortality is to be expected, since these little guys have such a tenuous hold on life. Five a day out of four or five hundred fish seems insignificant, but at that rate, over 20 days, the total mortality would be 100 fish, around 25%. Also, in the first few days the larvae are so tiny and have such little mass that a dead larvae is difficult to see in the detritus on the bottom and quickly decomposes. One would notice a large number of dead larvae in the first few days, but it is easy to overlook those that do die when it is only a few.

There are at least 400 of the 14 day old larvae in the 20 gallon tank. Only half of them can be seen at any one time. They have started swimming around the tank in a counter clockwise pattern, not regimented, of course, but there is a definite circular pattern of movement. Once in a while one of the larvae goes berserk and swims very rapidly and seemingly without direction or purpose into the surface or the bottom of the tank, or along the side, and then sort of shakes it out and resumes normal swimming and feeding. I have no idea why they do that.

I fed wild plankton and brine shrimp this morning. That was really a great plankton pull last Sunday, a really dense collection of copepods. They form little clouds in the rearing tank and the larvae swim though the clouds of copepods, one on each side of the tank, and feed as they move along. I have not fed rotifers in a couple of days.

I went to All Seas to deliver some books this morning and brought along 4 of the juvenile orchid dottybacks. They were happy to have them but would pay only $10.00 each, which is the price wholesalers pay to collectors. Which is OK, because like all good business people, wholesalers and retailers have to know what a product is worth and buy it at a price that will enable them to make a profit when they sell it. The fish business also has to cover losses from fish mortality in the price of the fish that do survive, a cost that is eventually passed on to the final consumer, the hobbyist. It's too bad, however, that tank reared marine fish do not command a premium.

Raising fish on such a small scale sure won't pay the bills, or even just the cost of rearing them because of the intense work load required to breed them. Also, if any scarce, but popular, fish becomes common in the trade because they are tank bred in numbers, then the price will inevitably decline and it will be even more difficult to make the rearing effort pay off. I guess a good fish breeder has to also be a good business person as well.

I did a really dumb thing this morning! As my mother used to say, "You should have your head examined." Me that is, not you. But then who knows, maybe you did a dumb thing today too, and your mother probably would have said the same thing to you. But anyway, my next project is to work with the pigmy angels in the genus *Centropyge*. The pigmy angels have not yet been reared in captivity, as far as I know, because although they are not difficult to spawn in tanks, the pelagic egg of these species is rather small, around 500 microns, I believe, and the larvae are correspondingly small and may have serious dietary restrictions. Rearing them will not be easy and will probably not closely follow any previous rearing technique. After all, since rearing marine fish is an exercise in masochism, why should my next project be an easy fish?

Actually, I would like to work with the flame angel, *Centropyge loriculus*, if I can find a few small individuals; but since I saw some small cherubfish, *C. argi*, at All Seas, I thought I'd get a couple and see if they would mature and spawn. I picked out the largest and the smallest juveniles that I could find and brought them home. The theory is that the largest one will become the male and the smaller the female. The large one was about one and one half inches and the smaller about one and one fourth inches long. So far, so good. I realized that I would have to set them up in a tank with a pair of clownfish, *Amphiprion ocellaris*, and a pair of orchid dottybacks, *Pseudochromis fridmani*, since I have pairs of these fish in all four brood stock tanks, but since these are all very different fish, I thought that they would be able to coexist.

My big mistake was putting the pygmies in with the spawning pair of *P. fridmani*. I should have put them in with one of the immature pairs, but Tank 3 was the easiest to see and work with and I thought that the pigmy angels would be the most at risk if there was any difficulty. Well the largest pigmy angel and the male orchid dottyback went round and round and didn't really hurt each other but there was some strong interaction. Things may have settled down and the fish may have learned to suffer each others existence, and may yet do so, but the male dottyback somehow, in the heat of the moment, got it's head tangled up in the rocks and may have injured it's eye or jaw. He was swimming awkwardly about the tank shortly after this encounter and is now holed up in the rock, not acting normally at all.

I may have to move the pigmy angels to the next tank, probably should, but I would have to pull all the rocks from the tank to catch them. Maybe if he survives, however, they will learn to ignore each other. I'll keep a close eye on them. The pigmy angels will be the subject of another journal as they mature and begin to spawn. Hopefully, I'll get a pair or two of some other species as well.

Unfortunately, today is the day that the pair of dotty-backs are scheduled to spawn. I doubt that that will happen now, but I would not have been able to rear the spawn anyway, so it is not a great loss. If I were commercial, however, I would be kicking myself for many days for the inexcusable mistake of messing up a spawning pair. This rearing journal, however, will soon be wrapped up when the Great Run is over, another 15 days or so.

10:45 PM

Amazing! At 8:00 PM, before the lights went out, the male dottyback was under the rocks, still hiding from the pigmy angels, and the female was moseying about looking lost. The lights went out as usual, the bulbs over the tanks off at about 9 PM and the algae lights out at about 9:30 PM. Then, when I looked at the tank at 10:30 PM after the lights were out, both male and female dottybacks were in the den and they had spawned! I don't know if the eggs are fertilized or not, but since the male was in the den also, I presume that fertilization did take place. The pigmy angels can't get into the den, the opening is too small for them, so tomorrow should be interesting.

August 20, 1996, 10:30 AM

Day 15 of the Great Run! Fear and Trepidation! More mortality than I have yet seen. Sixteen dead larvae on the bottom, many of them the larger larvae. DON'T THESE FISH KNOW WHO I AM? How dare they die on me? After all this heroic effort to get these guys through in fantastic numbers in a relatively tiny tank, how dare the gods of fish culture mess me up? Actually, I think it may be a bacterial problem. A few of the weak and struggling larvae I can see with the magnifying glass have a white nose and I can see signs of tissue death in the body musculature. This may also be associated with the "berserk" behavior I frequently see in some larvae. Sometimes in their mad dash about the tank they seem to run into the bottom or a side and may injure their nose and create an opening for bacterial infection.

Most of the larvae, however, are still strong and vigorous and are feeding well. I fed the last of the great plankton tow and a fair amount of brine shrimp napulii this morning. I'm sure that part of the problem has been the relative lack of water changes that I have accomplished on this run. Rearing only a few larvae in a tank does not degrade the water nearly as much as working with several hundred larvae. I will do a 50% change today and add another dose of streptomycin and neomycin after the change. It's too bad that this tank is not on a system, water change would then be easy. Many of the larvae are pushing a half inch now and are starting to pick up a few of the magenta pigment spots, which is a good sign at day 15.

The male dottyback is in with his eggs this morning and I haven't seen him out yet, even during feeding. The other fish, including the female dottyback, are just cruising the tank without a care in the world.

I collected a goodly number of rotifers also and have them under enrichment for a few hours. I'll hold them and feed them after the bottom cleaning and water change.

12:30 PM

The water change is underway. It will take about 45 minutes to drain 5 gallons from the tank though the little air tubing siphon, but this way I won't pull out any larval fish, any live ones that is. I did siphon the bottom and removed the dead ones. There is still a potload of larvae in the tank and I hope I get a couple of hundred through. We will see, however, considering the food that goes through the fish and the water, that is quite a bio load for a 20 gallon tank.

In the "My isn't that interesting", department, I noticed a number of tiny "eggs", about 5 or 6 hundred microns in diameter, in the tank after this last plankton tow. At first I thought that they were invertebrate eggs of some type because they were different colors, translucent to cream color. They floated in the meniscus at the edge of the water's surface along the tank side. Then I noticed that they were different sizes, which I thought was odd since eggs of any one species are always close to the same size. The next day they were still there, with no sign of development or any internal structures. I pulled out a few and they were hard and could not be crushed between my fingernails. Days later they are still present. The only thing that I think they could be are little resin beads from a water softener or other chemical treatment system. They may have been released from some marina or boat water purification system. It's possible that these tiny beads could be ingested by larval fish or invertebrates and cause mortality that would never be noticed.

August 21, 1996, 3:00 PM

Day 16 of the Great Run! This was the day, in the runs before use of wild plankton, that the last larval dottyback to survive would exit the stage from the busy play of life. Mortality was relatively light last night, however, only about 6 fish. There are still hundreds of larvae, maybe three hundred or so?, actively swimming about the tank. They vary in size from one fourth to one half inch long, the size differential that occurs in larval fish from the same spawn in the same tank never ceases to amaze me. The guts were empty this morning, no sign of the brine shrimp that I fed a few hours before the lights went out last night. I fed brine shrimp napulii again this morning and then went for plankton at 10:30 AM. The plankton was good, even though I was a little early and didn't catch the incoming tide at the optimum time. Only one troll asleep under the bridge at this late hour. I should have enough wild plankton so that with a little brine shrimp, I can feed the tank for about three days. There is a time, incidently, when one stops feeding the tank, that is trying to keep a certain level of food organisms in the tank, and begins to feed the fish instead. With the orchid dottyback, this occurs about day 10, although it is a gradual development, but now at day 16, this is very much the case.

The few, 5 or 6, larvae remaining from the previous hatch, now 21 days old, are entering metamorphosis at about 5/8 inch (15 mm) long. I slop a little plankton to them and also give them brine shrimp napulii, and in general sort of ignore them since I am so consumed by the Great Run. Once they get into the juvenile stage they grow very fast. The juveniles that I moved into the 30 gallon tank about 17 days ago are almost large enough to sell. The tank is alive with brilliant purple flashes. A spectacular sight! The oldest juveniles, about 35 of them, seem to be nearing maturity. I have sold a few, but I've been holding them for Jeff. I'll have to contact him tomorrow and see if I can move these out and clear up the 20 gallon grow-out tank.

August 22, 1996, 10:45 PM

Day 17 of the Great Run! Still looking good. Only 3 mortalities this morning. There must be at least 300 larvae still going round the tank. I don't think I'll get them all through, but I don't see very many larvae with problems at this point, so I am wildly optimistic. I do see the same sort of thing I saw in the big runs of gray and French angels. Most of the larvae are "normal" in size for the age of the run, but there are a few that are noticeably larger than the others and perhaps a few more that are quite a bit smaller than the "normal" sized larvae. Most of the mortality comes from the larger and smaller fish. Some of the smaller fish may drag out the larval stage 10 days longer than the "average" larvae and the larger fish may go through metamorphosis four or five days earlier than average. This can be a problem when you're working in small tanks and need to move the juveniles out before all the larvae have become juveniles.

I think maybe that the time around day 13, 14, and 15 is a time of developmental tribulation for the larvae. It may have something to do with organ development, enzyme changes, or just changes in food organism requirements, but they seem more delicate at this point. It may also just have been a problem period during this run.

I fed wild plankton and brine shrimp napulii this morning. I also made a good collection of rotifers and they are under enrichment at this time. I think all but the smallest larvae are past the rotifer stage now, but I will feed rotifers with the wild plankton this afternoon anyway. The outside rotifer culture has come up very well since I paid more attention to feeding it and keeping its bottom clean.

8:30 PM

Day 17 is almost over, just fed a bit of brine shrimp. I'm saving the rest of the wild plankton till tomorrow morning. I won't get any more plankton till late tomorrow or the next morning, tides depending. There are quite a few of the larvae that are now picking up a bit more of the orchid color and are staying near the bottom, sure signs of

impending metamorphosis. It is still very early in the transformation process but it is a good sign that they are growing well.

August 23, 1996, 5:00 PM

Day 18 of the Great Run! There were about 6 mortalities in the tank today. Not good, but not bad. The larvae
are getting big and getting color. Not the real vivid magenta of the juveniles, but a definite light brownish red
tinge. Many of them are hanging out near the bottom as
well, but they are still moving fast and metamorphosis is
still in the future. I fed raw shrimp particles first thing this
morning and they seemed to take most of them. I could tell
that some of the shrimp particles did wind up on the bottom, and by watching closely with the magnifying glass, I
could see that some of the larvae would line up a shrimp
particle, set themselves to take it, and then break off when
it didn't move. They do the same thing to brine shrimp
and copepods, and then when the food organism makes a
move, the larval fish strikes and takes it. Other larvae were
taking the shrimp particles, however. The tank is still full
of larvae, it will be interesting to count them in 10 days or
so when the juveniles are moved into a larger tank.

Didn't make any entries this morning because Barb
made me go and get a haircut. Also got the mail and went
to the grocery store. Real life often enters into the world of
the marine aquarist/ fish breeder, but not without a strug-
gle.

Got plankton this afternoon. I could have waited until
tomorrow to get plankton, but the tides are such that getting plankton about mid afternoon is best right now, and
tomorrow is Saturday, and there are usually some fisher-
folk along the seawall on Saturday, and I wouldn't want to

get a hook caught in Julian's plankton net. I also hate to fight for a spot along the seawall. And the questions, "Whut kina bait you tryin to get with that thing?" are never ending.

The rotifer cultures are winding down. I'm not paying very much attention to them these days except to feed them and keep some going. I probably won't be doing any more rearing until the pigmy angels start breeding, so I will have the time to finish up the breeding book and maybe the Data Book also. I'll just keep the rotifers going at a subsistence level so I can crank them up again when I start breeding again.

The eggs that were laid in the male dottyback's den the night of the day that the pigmy angels were introduced into the tank apparently were not fertile for I saw no development and they only lasted a couple of days. The female dottyback and the angels seem to get along fine, no harassment at all, but the male is staying in his den and seldom, if ever, ventures into the tank. I have not seen him eat since the angels came into the tank. I may have to intervene again if he does not come around in a day or two, and move the angels to a different tank. Like I said, If I was a commercial breeder I would have a sore butt because I kicked it so much.

August 24, 1996, 11:55 AM

Day 19 of the Great Run! Two or three more mortalities, no big deal. Many of the larvae are down near the bottom and are starting to look more seriously reddish. They turn a sort of dark reddish color in a translucent cast before the vivid magenta color develops. I just did a bottom siphon and am now changing about one third of the water. I'll put in some PVC bottom structures today since so many of them are now orienting to the bottom. I fed some brine shrimp, some shrimp particles, which they take but not avidly like the complete juveniles do, and some wild plankton. I'll feed a little more brine shrimp today and some more wild plankton. I'll save about a third of the plankton for tomorrow.

The plankton was clear with no algal bloom, it's really been pretty good for the last part of the summer, but it wasn't very rich with zooplankton this last tow. I took a salinity reading and it was down to 24 ppt, which explained the lack of zooplankton. It was nearly high tide and that was a rather low salinity for high tide water. They must have released a good bit of fresh water from the flood control gates. I'll have to call the flood control people and tell them not to release water when I plan to get plankton. (Yeah, sure) Even though it wasn't the richest plankton, it still did very well. I'm sure that this run had more wild plankton than was necessary for survival, but then I wanted to make sure that I got as many through as possible, sort of a benchmark run.

I have been reusing the plankton water and so far no problems. I use chlorine to sterilize and to oxidize all the organics in the water. I put a good dose of chlorine, about 10 ppm or a little higher in the bucket after all the plankton has been removed over a 53 micron sieve and let it sit for 24 to 48 hours. Within a few hours after the chlorine treatment the water is crystal clear, and remains so for the rest of the treatment. The chlorine is removed with sodium thiosulphate after a day or so and I check and adjust the salinity before putting it into the water reservoir.

The 4 or 5 fish in the 24 day old run (today) are now well into the juvenile stage. They are full colored and posturing above the PVC habitats. A couple are still in the late larval or post larval stage, but are hanging out on the bottom now. It will be most neat to have two or three hundred juvenile orchid dottybacks in that twenty gallon tank and this is now only about 5 days away, if all goes well.

2:30 PM

Finished the water change and the late larval dottybacks look happy. Also added a bit more streptomycin and neomycin, to make up the water change, and because there are so many in that little tank. I put in one rock and four PVC pipe habitats so that they will have a place to go during metamorphosis.

August 25, 1996, 11:30 AM

Day 20 of the Great Run! A bit of mortality this morning, I counted 13 dead larvae on the bottom. Metamorphosis is closer, however, a lot of reddish color in the larvae this morning, and more of them are spending time near the bottom. The few remaining from the run just before the great run are full juveniles now at 25 days. Big changes in the great run should occur in the next 5 days. I fed the last of the wild plankton this morning and will now have to rely on brine shrimp napulii until I get more plankton, perhaps tomorrow afternoon. The tides are such that I have to go at 4 or 5 in the morning (God forbid) or 4 or 5 in the afternoon. I will also use some particle foods, washed raw shrimp, and ground flake food since the larvae should be big enough now to take at least some of the particles.

The male orchid dottyback came out of his den to feed a bit today, but as soon as one of the pigmy angels would swim by he would dive back into his hole. I don't know why they have him so intimidated, they really don't pay the dottybacks much attention. They don't nip at them, but they don't swim out of their way either. Maybe in a few days, he will be less intimidated by them and perhaps re-kindle an interest in breeding. I'll leave them together for a few more days anyway, since he has started feeding again.

August 26, 1996, 10:45 AM

Day 21 of the Great Run! About 6 mortalities this morn-ing. I hope that I don't get any increase over this rate in the next 6 to 8 days. By then they should be through metamor-phosis, at least most of them. Most of the larvae have no-ticeable pigment now and are a half inch or so long. None have become juveniles yet, but it isn't far off for many of them.

There is a slight algal bloom in the tank as of yesterday afternoon. This should not be a problem, unless, of course, it gets very heavy and then dies or uses up all the oxygen at night, but I think I could either filter it out or change water if it got too heavy. It had diminished somewhat this morning. I have no more wild plankton and the tides are not favorable until late this afternoon. They are large enough now, however, to subsist on brine shrimp, and maybe a few rotifers for the smaller ones, although those that are not over 7 or 8 mm by now probably won't make it through all the way. There are only a few of these, how-ever, and their loss will not greatly affect the total numbers that survive.

The poor beleaguered male orchid dottyback stays in his den all day. I did see him dart out to feed a couple of times yesterday, but as soon as he spots the pigmy angel, he blasts back into his hole. Interestingly, they, the dotty-backs, spawned again yesterday. The male was curled up over a big spawn last night and it looks good. Evidently the female, heavy with eggs, just went into his den and they spawned without all that chasing and leading that they used to do. I put my ear to the tank and I could here her saying, "Come on, Bill, pull yourself together. Get out of this funk. Those angels could care less about you, all they are interested in is that nasty old algae growing on the rocks. They're dumb fish anyway. You're much prettier and faster. And if you don't shape up I'll just my change my gender, and that will really shake you up!" Evidently fish are a lot like people, and then, maybe not.

August 27, 1996, 11:50 AM

Day 22 of the Great Run! So far, so good. There is still a bit of an algal bloom in the tank, but the fish look good. More are near the bottom and they are redder than the day before. The wild plankton yesterday was good, salinity is still a bit low. I guess that they (the flood control folks) are keeping water levels low in the county because of the hurricane, Edwardo, churning up the Atlantic about 1000 miles to the southeast. There is a chance that it will get us, but it is too far away for any predictions yet.

There were about 6 mortalities on the bottom this morning; there seem to be somewhere between 5 to 10 every day. However, the tank is still very full of late larvae, and I'm sure, baring catastrophe, that I will get a large number through. I looked at one of the recently dead larvae under the dissecting scope and the gut was full of partially digested brine shrimp and a few copepods. There was no obvious cause of death. The liver was normal size, although the gall bladder was enlarged, not unusual for tank raised fish, and there was no oil or fat accumulation in the liver. It would be interesting to compare livers of fish fed exclusively on brine shrimp napulii with those of fish fed on wild plankton. Histological examination of liver tissue would be the best way to analyze the tissue structure. But then, fish die, especially larval fish and it is very difficult to pinpoint a cause for most incidental larval fish mortality.

Today I will take 15 pairs down to Jeff. It will be "fun" getting the fish out of the rocks. That is my next task of the day.

9:00 PM

I got the little guys out of the holes in the rock and took them down to Jeff. There were 21 left in the 20 gallon grow-out tank, and so I had to add 9 from the younger batch in the 30 gallon tank. The younger ones had grown rapidly, however, and at 51 days they were quite large enough to be the smaller fish in a pair, in fact the largest of them are developing male characteristics.

August 28, 1996, 1:15 PM

Day 23 and the Great Run is in trouble. The little old lady almost backed into the airplane propeller. DISASTER came close and I'm still not out of the woods. I looked in the 20 gallon tank this morning and saw some dead larvae, about 10 to 12, but the water was dark with an algal bloom and the live larvae were hanging limply in the water column or laying listlessly on the bottom. Even the barnacles were all closed up and not pumping. I immediately turned up the air release in the tank, did a 75% water change, and watched anxiously. The larvae did pick up and most got back up into the water column and began a search for food. I put a little brine shrimp into the tank and most of them began to feed. I felt the problem was either low oxygen caused by an air release that had slowed a bit, probably because of gradual clogging and the now rather dense algal bloom using up the oxygen overnight, or... the dreaded toxic tank syndrome.

Well I hadn't put all this effort into this run over the last 23 days just to let Mother Nature flush me down her drain that easily. I know that if the problem is the toxic tank syndrome (although my use of streptomycin reduces that possibility, the very high density of larvae, also makes that more likely), then the water change would only buy me some time, maybe a day or two. Also the only way that I have ever found to save fish for sure in the early stages of toxic tank syndrome is to move them to a new, unaffected tank. So I made up some more saltwater, I used up most of what I had stored on the water change, and cleaned up the 20 gallon tank that I had just sold the fish out of yesterday, and made up another 20 gallon larval tank with the new water and a new dose of streptomycin.

The larvae were far too numerous to try to move them by capturing them in a baby food jar, and I did not want to introduce much of the water from the affected tank into the new tank, so I had to net the late larvae from the old tank. Many of the larvae are now in the early stages of metamorphosis, staying on the bottom and beginning to pick up the dark magenta color. I filled a bowl with the new water (I didn't really want to use water that had been made up only a couple of hours ago, but there was little choice at this point), netted about 20 late larvae and placed them in the bowl. They would either live or die. Fortunately, they lived and were quite active swimming about the bowl for 10 or 15 minutes. I placed them in the new tank and observed them for another 15 minutes and they seemed to be adjusting quite well.

3:30 PM

The larvae in the old 20 were not doing well and the water continued to cloud a bit. I bit the bullet and moved all the larvae to then new 20. I counted 40 dead on the bottom of the old 20. I know that there will be considerable mortality in the fish that I moved, but there was no choice, it was move them or lose them! They are feeding in the new tank and most of them seem to have made the move without expiring. I know that I must have moved over 400 of them, so we will see how many survive. The Great Run goes on, a little ragged about the edges and in a new tank, but it is still rolling. I'll get some plankton on them tomorrow morning.

August 29, 1996, 11:15 AM

Day 24 of the Great Run! A little shaky, and frayed around the edges, but still a Great Run. There were about 30 dead in the new tank this morning, counted on the bottom of a bucket after siphoning detritus and dead larvae from the tank bottom. That, added to the 40 counted yesterday in the old tank, makes 70 counted larvae lost to the probably toxic tank syndrome in the old tank. I was lucky that I caught it so early and that the losses were not greater. The tank is still alive with larvae and now about 10 or so juveniles that have recently gone through metamorphosis. I am sure that if I had not moved them the loss would have been almost 100 percent instead of the loss of maybe 20 or 25 percent. The difference in behavior of the larvae is amazing. They were on the bottom or swimming weakly in a head up position and looked almost partially paralyzed in the old tank, and now, in the new tank, they are zipping about the tank, swimming in a horizontal position and looking strong again.

I got plankton early this morning, a good tow, strong full moon tidal current, no algae blooms and good zooplankton content. The larvae are feeding avidly on wild plankton and brine shrimp napulii. Rotifers are no

longer needed and I have stopped maintaining feeder rotifer cultures. I will try to keep a seed culture of algae and rotifers going so that I can crank them up again when they
are needed. I did not finish the rotifer culture media experiments, but I did do enough to know how to maintain a
good rotifer culture with a V8® and cornstarch media. It
will work, but it takes a bit more maintenance than yeast
cultures, and a bit less than an algae culture base. Doubt-
less, the algae culture base produces the cleanest and best
rotifers as food organisms, but the V8® technique, and the
yeast cultures, are good supplements to the algae culture
and can be used to save rotifer production and larval fish
when algae cultures crash.

Wild plankton seems to be important (at least at this
point) to the survival of a number of species of marine
tropical fish larvae in relatively large scale culture attempts. What I would do, if I were to go back into commercial marine tropical fish culture (besides finish up my
Ph.D. in masochism), would be to set up three or four
large fiberglass vats or tubs, 300 to 400 gallons or so each,
fill them with seawater and start an algal culture in them.
Then, when the algae culture is well advanced, begin to
take daily plankton tows and deposit them into one of the
algae culture vats. I would also probably treat the plankton
tows with copper, being careful not to introduce much copper into the holding vat, and also sieve the tows through a
200 or 500 micron screen.

The required plankton for the larval fish and invertebrate cultures would be taken from the these vats as
needed and this would stabilize plankton production by allowing some reproduction of copepods, provide nutrition
to the holding plankton, and keep plankton available on
days when it is not practical to make to make tows. The

vats would be run cyclically, each one holding a working plankton population for one or two weeks, or whatever works best, and the other vats either being flushed and cleaned or in the process of building an algal bloom. Antibiotics could be used if necessary to reduce bacterial toxins in the holding vats, but I would hope that it would not be necessary. I think such a process would smooth out the rough edges of plankton availability and provide a very important nutritional link before/between rotifers and brine shrimp for many species of larval fish.

5:30 PM

Tonight is the night of a thousand deaths! The spawn of 8/25 is due to hatch tonight and it looks good, a lot of little eyes looking out of those little eggs. It kills me not to set up the old 20 gallon tank and try to bring them through, but I just don't have the time. Also we have a number of trips coming up in September, October, and November and I just can't put in the concentrated day to day effort that rearing them requires. The 55 has 14 near adults in it now, the 30 has probably about 30 older juveniles (53 days old and really big for that age) and of course the new 20 now has about 300? that are just turning a vivid magenta. I cleaned the glass on all the tanks today and the swarms of those vivid magenta orchid dottybacks are so beautiful that they take your breath away. But I have done what I set out to do. I know how to rear the orchid dottyback in large numbers, and I have the data and the photos to publish, so I have to let it go. There is still a lot of work to be done on this species, and on others, to fine tune the rearing process, but this will have to wait till later.

August 30, 1996, 9:30 AM

Day 25 of the Great Run! Last night was indeed a night of 1000 deaths. The tank was alive with larval *Pseudochromis fridmani* at 10:30 PM. It was a good hatch and I made no attempt to save it, alas.

There were about 6 dead larvae this morning. Fifteen or so are now juveniles, it looks like about 40 are well colored with a rusty red shade and a couple of hundred ? are still in the late larval condition. This will be, if all continues to go well, the largest numbers from one hatch that I have brought through, but it won't be as spectacular as I had hoped. Still a couple of hundred isn't bad, and I'm sure that I could do much better under better rearing conditions.

I fed wild plankton and brine shrimp napulii to the larvae this morning. They still take a lot of food organisms. I think they would start taking shrimp particles well at this point. I may try that a bit later.

August 31, 1996, 10:40 AM

Day 26 of the Great Run! Only 4 or 5 were dead on the bottom today and most of these are the small and the weak. There is always a group of larvae in any large run that do not grow very fast, and although healthy in the early and middle stages of the rearing run, they are still in the mid larval stage when the environment of the tank turns from planktonic to benthic. The turning of the tank from a water column environment to a bottom environment occurs gradually, and with the orchid dottyback, some time after day 18 and extends to about day 26. The majority of the larvae take on color and begin to associate with the bottom and sides of the tank, and with any structures or rocks that may be put into the tank at about this time. They feed on brine shrimp, shrimp particles, dry food particles, and begin to feed on benthic food particles.

Because of the food change, the slow growing larvae that are still primarily pelagic no longer have the necessary planktonic environment in the tank, begin to decline, and eventually die. In larger, higher tanks, however, especially tanks 74 to 200 gallons, the planktonic environment can be maintained much longer in the upper reaches of the tank and more of these slow growers can be weaned through the larval stages.

The late larvae, post larvae (the rusty red mid meta-morphic larvae), and the early juveniles are all looking good in the new tank. They survived the move very well (these orchid dottybacks are hardy fish!), and I would ex-pect relatively little additional mortality, except, perhaps, some of the less developed larvae that require constant mid water feeding. I fed the last of the wild plankton and brine shrimp napulii this morning. I'll do a little particu-late food and more brine shrimp later on today.

9

September 1996 -

Hundreds of Dottybacks!

September 2, 1996, 11:20 PM

Day 28 of the Great Run! Oops, missed a day. The kids were over for the Sunday before Labor Day and I was busy. Took my grandson Winston, 7 ½ years old, out in the canoe fishing. We caught 3 bass and he got to run the electric motor and steer the canoe the whole way. The Dolphins won their first game of season also, so it was a good day.

Very little mortality in the last two days. More than half of them are now juveniles. The bottom is covered with all these little magenta flashes darting between the PVC pipes. There are still a lot of the rusty red post larvae and quite a few of those that have yet to pick up the red of the late larvae stage. Some of these guys will make it through but others just won't find the right food in the right amount. The food organisms, brine shrimp and plankton, don't stay in the water column very long anymore. As soon as it is introduced, the post larvae and the juveniles clean it out and the less developed, mid water larvae have only a brief period to feed. I will add a live rock or two to this tank today and also the sponge filter that was in that tank with the 20 fish that I sold last week. I put it in the 55 to keep it active. This will make it harder for the less developed larvae to survive, but that tank really needs some filtration now that most of the fish are juveniles.

The original pair are now grandparents! I noticed that the male of the pair in tank number 1 was spending a lot of time in the PVC pipe den that I made for him, so I looked in with the flashlight and there was a little egg ball, probably about 2 days old. How about that, spawning at 4 ½ months old. The original pair spawned again last Saturday, 8/31. The male still rarely comes out of the den, he is still intimidated by the pigmy angels. He darts out once in a while to pick up a bit of food but then scrambles back in even if the pigmy angels are not in his vicinity.

September 3, 1996, 1:15 PM

Day 29 of the Great Run! Almost all of the *P. fridmani* are now juveniles or rusty red post larvae. A few are still in the late larval stage and they are having a hard time finding enough food. The big guys scarf it up very quickly and there isn't enough left in the water for the less developed larvae. The water is still a little cloudy, even after the small sponge filter was put in the tank. I will have to watch the situation very closely. If the tank were on a system, which it should be, then I would have started a trickle change a few days ago.

I cleaned out the 30 gallon rotifer tank that was on the patio and I may set this up to take the 14, now adults, in the 55 gallon grow out tank. Then when the 55 is free, I can put all the little ones from this last spawn in there for grow out.

The second generation spawn in tank #1 hatched last night. Alas, so many nights of a 1000 deaths. There were a lot of little larvae in the tank at 11:00 PM but I had to abandon them to the cruel world of the aquarium. I hated to do that, but I just don't have the time to rear more of the orchid dottybacks. In fact, this journal will end when I pull the last hatch out of the 20, count them, and put them in the 55 grow out.

September 4, 1996, 2:05 PM

Day 30 of the Great Run! I guess day 30 is a significant day in the run, almost all of the fish are now juveniles although there are still about 25 or so that have not transformed yet. These very late larvae should either die or make the trip through metamorphosis in the next few days. I will set up the 30 gallon tank for the largest fish that are now in the 55 and then be ready to move the Great Run as soon they are all juveniles.

The plankton this morning, probably the last tow for the dottyback rearing, was spectacular. Perhaps the swells from Fran, all the way on the other side of the Bahamas, pushed oceanic water with its oceanic plankton into the inlet. This is probably the case since the salinity was 33 ppt, almost full oceanic salinity. If all plankton tows were this good, rotifers and brine shrimp would not be needed at all in the larvae rearing regime. I may even freeze some since I can't use it all before it dies anyway.

September 5, 1996, 10:15 AM

Day 31 of the Great Run! No mortality this morning. The juveniles are getting bigger and bigger, Most of them are between 3/4 and 1 inch long. There are still a number of them, perhaps 25 that are in the late larval stages. As soon as these are juveniles, baring any loss of water quality in the 20 that a water change can't fix, I will move them into the 55. Today I'll prepare the 30 and move the 14 adults to make the 55 ready. I should have a lot of little dottybacks to take up to the MACNA 8 convention in October.

That was superb plankton that I collected yesterday. The copepods were very abundant and just a small fraction of the stored plankton fills the 20 gallon larval/early juvenile tank. I am winding down the algae and rotifer cultures, I'll try to keep a small culture of each going so that I can crank them up again when and if I start on the pigmy angels. The clownfish I got from Aqualife last November are large now and should start spawning soon. If I can work it in, I will rear a few batches of them just to get the pictures and perhaps a daily journal for the clownfish.

September 6, 1996, 10:45 AM

Day 32 of the Great Run! It's not over yet. I guess it's not over till the fat fish jumps. It's very interesting. There seems to be two distinct groups of fish in this run. The first, and most numerous, went through metamorphosis starting at about day 20 and extending to about day 28. It didn't take 8 days for a single fish to go through metamorphosis, more like two or three at the most, but the major group went through it at some point from day 20 through day 28. The second group is just now approaching metamorphosis at day 30 to 32 and judging from their size and color, I don't expect all of them to go through metamorphosis until day 34 to 36. The two groups I mentioned are not clear and distinct, but are more like two peaks on a curve. This is just an empirical observation and not an analytical result. It may very well be an artifact of the artificial rearing environment and not be associated with any genetic variation controlling growth rates in the larval fish.

Anyway, I changed 5 gallons of water in the larval tank, about one third, and I will hold off moving them until all or almost all are into the juvenile stage. I did not add streptomycin this time since I plan to move them within a few days. I added algae culture to the last fourth of the great plankton tow in hopes of enriching the copepods and keeping them till the end of the day. I fed some wild plankton and brine shrimp napulii this morning and they all look fat and happy. I also set up the algae and rotifer cultures in maintenance mode until the pigmy angels or clownfish start spawning and I have to go back into production mode. Maintenance mode is just working with gallon jars, cleaning and starting new cultures once a week or so just to keep them going at low levels.

The new spawning pair of 5 month old orchid dottybacks (pair # 2) have spawned again yesterday, 9/5. The male is guarding a cute little egg ball. It is about half the size of the egg balls that the original pair produce as full adults. Someday it would be fun to rear a batch from the second generation.

September 7, 1996, 11:45 AM

Day 33 of the Great Run! Finally ran out of the plankton from that last great tow. I set up some of the copepods from that tow in a tray with green water just to see how they do. There are still about 50 larvae that are not yet juveniles. Most of these are now in the rusty red post larval stage, so within a few days they should all be juveniles. I probably won't get any more plankton and I'll rely on grated, particulate shrimp and brine shrimp napulii to bring them all through to saleable size.

The original male is now in an uneasy coexistence with the pigmy angels, these are *Centropyge argi* by the way. He comes out to feed frequently now and spawning is back to normal, they produced a good size egg ball yesterday, 9/6.

September 9, 1996, 10:00 AM

Day 35 of the Great Run! Missed a day yesterday, must be sort of running down on this journal. I'm still waiting on the last of the post larvae to become juveniles. There are about 20 that are refusing to metamorphose completely. They are staying in that rusty red phase. I am also losing a few of these "late bloomers" from time to time. There were about 12 that were dead yesterday AM. I think I will move them out today anyway. The bigger juveniles seem to get the food long before the post larvae can get to them anyway, and the post larvae just might do better in the larger grow-out tank. Also, Bill Addison of C-Quest is sending me a small pair of *Pseudochromis paccagnellae*, the bicolor dottyback, perhaps today depending on Hortense, the hurricane that is churning up the Caribbean south of Puerto Rico, and if they come, I will set them up in the twenty that the last run of the orchid dottybacks now occupy.

The spawn of the second generation disappeared over the last day or two. Evidently is not unusual for the spawns over the first few months to be sporadic in survival. The PVC pipe habitats I built for the new pairs work well, but I think that they would be better if I drilled a few holes in the pipes to get better water circulation through the den. I will do this when I get the time. It is easy to spawn these guys, but rearing takes a lot of time and effort.

The male pigmy angel and the male orchid dottyback are still interacting in the brood stock tank. He comes out much more frequently and is evidently feeding enough to maintain normal activity and metabolism. The male, or presumed male, pigmy angel chases after the male orchid dottyback when he wanders too far away from his den, and the dottyback swims rapidly away and avoids the pigmy. The pigmy does not bother the female dottyback or either of the two clownfish, however.

September 10, 1996, 4:10 PM

Day 36 of the Great Run! I moved all the rusty red post larvae and the magenta juveniles out of the 20 gallon larval tank and into the 55 gallon grow-out tank yesterday PM. There were more than I thought. A total of 275 juveniles and 76 post larvae. This is a total of 351 fish from a single spawn in a 20 gallon larval tank. Not bad. The juveniles settled into the rocks very well and the post larvae swam above the rocks. They quickly started feeding on shaved shrimp and new hatch brine shrimp. I'm sure that they all will not survive to salable size, but I should get at least 300 through to sub adult size. They were about 3/4 of an inch long, some a bit more and some a bit less.

Lets see, now that's about 350 orchid dottybacks from one spawn reared in a 20 gallon tank. The going wholesale price is $20.00 each (although this price is dropping rapidly as more tank reared dottybacks reach the market and as the number of collectors in the Red Sea increases), so that makes this rearing potentially worth $7,000.00. Now if I set up 10 twenty gallon tanks, that would be $70,000.00 in about 45 days. Hmmmm.... Actually this is an example of how not to think when rearing marine tropical fish. It can get you in a great deal of trouble because it is never that simple. One can quickly get one's fanny in a financial sling, and wind up holding an occupational tiger by the tail. It has been great fun, however, and also a lot of work. I have learned a lot and I'm looking forward to rearing the pigmy angels, but not just yet. Oh great god Neptune, let me get at least one book finished before they spawn.

Now I must go and prepare about 6 ice cube trays of shaved shrimp, new hatch brine shrimp, and some flake food. We are going away for three days, a writers conference, and the neighbors are going to feed the fish. If I have everything frozen up in ice cubes, then it is a simple matter to drop an ice cube or two into each tank and the fish will take it from there. The ice cubes melt over a period of a few minutes so the food doesn't just flood into the tank all at once. The worst thing about feeding this way is that sometimes the shaved shrimp tends to float instead of sinking and the fish don't always get it all. If they are hungry enough, however, they will take it off the surface.

September 11, 1996, 11:10 PM

Day 37 of the Great Run! It's late at night and I'm tired. The fish are all OK and all settled in their respective tanks. No mortality anywhere. I got everything set up now for the trip. Barb and I will be going to the Florida Outdoor Writer's convention at Daytona Beach over the next few days and our new neighbors will be feeding the fish for us. Everything should be all right, the food cubes seem to work fine. It will only be for three and a half days so what can go wrong? Don't answer that. I know what can go wrong, but one can't let a few fish run one's life, can one? Don't answer that either! Anyway, I'll let you know when we get back how the fish do without the fishmaster in attendance for a few day.

September 16, 1996, 10:00 AM

Day 42 of the Great Run, and the Great Run is over. Over, that is, in that there are no more larval or post larval fish. All are now either juveniles or history. We returned from the writers conference yesterday and, thanks to the neighbors, the fish survived quite well. The 55 grow-out is still full of juveniles (I can't count them, but I'm sure that at least 300 of the 346 that were placed in the tank still survive). There were no mortalities in the brood stock tanks and of the 5 late larval or post larval fish that remained in the 20, three survived and are now juveniles. They are not really strong juveniles yet, the color is still a bit washed out and they are relatively small. The larval stage in this run was abut 20 days for the most rapidly growing larvae and 40 days for the slowest growing larvae. Most of the larvae seemed to metamorphosis at about 25 days.

The conference went well. We learned a bit about the great new world of the Internet and electronic rights and traditional rights for writers. I got to play in the surf at Daytona Beach, something I haven't done for many years, and I became 59 years of age yesterday. The days and years mount up and before you know it, you're getting old, so do it now, tomorrow may be too late.

September 22, 1996, 2:00 PM

The culture room chores have declined to just routine maintenance of brood stock tanks, care and feeding of the juveniles, and maintenance of the base rotifer and algae cultures. This does not take too long and I have more time for writing. The last spawn of the original pair hatched last night. This was the largest hatch I have had yet and the larvae were very strong and active. It was with heavy heart that I left them to the cruel ecology of the brood stock tank system. C-Quest survived Hortense, but the dottyback pair Bill sent went astray. They evidently got mixed in with someone else's shipment for they never arrived at All Seas.

September 24, 1996, 5:00 PM

Well I spent all day in the fish room getting things cleaned up and organized. I moved out all the fish in the 30 gallon tank on the brood stock system. This was the tank that I put the second biggest run in a couple of months ago. I think I figured that there were about 70 fish in that run and they all went into this tank. I have taken fish from that tank, about 10 or 15, for sale a few weeks ago. Jeff wanted about 50 fish for display in the tank he is setting up in the Miami fish show and I thought that there should have been about 50 in this tank. There were exactly 50 in fact. He will be by tomorrow AM to pick them up.

Had the first little dottyback die of shock today. I moved the four that were very late post larvae from the great run that I left in the larval tank to a small 8 gallon larval tank. They had been feeding heavily on brine shrimp napulii and I moved them a bit roughly, netted into a bowl and then the bowl poured into the small tank. One of the small juveniles went into typical shock posture, head back, mouth open, fins extended and, unfortunately, heart stopped. He did not recover, so I put him under the scope and did an autopsy. The gut was full of brine shrimp napulii, very full, and unhatched brine shrimp cysts. There was very little oil in the brain and liver, which indicates that they are handling the brine shrimp diet fairly well. There may be deficiencies in their diet, but at least they don't accumulate oil the way that the clownfish do. I'm reasonably sure that if I had waited until the guts were empty, or close to it, that this incident of shock death would not have occurred.

The original pair spawned today, a nice big egg ball. It would be fun to rear them again but time does not allow it.

10

October 1996 -
Winding down

October 16, 1996, 11:30 PM

Back from MACNA VIII in Kansas City. It was a very good conference. I wound up presenting a video on the dottyback rearing work at the banquet and it seemed to be well received. The 351 juveniles from the Great Run have done well. I have seen only a few mortalities and I assume that survival has been very high so far. They are growing well. I took about 20 fairly large young adults and 30 late juveniles up to MACNA VIII and all of them were sold. I brought up some of them in the new Kordon Breathing Bags™ and I was amazed at how well these bags keep the fish for days without any concern except for temperature. Unfortunately, we lost quite a few of the little dottybacks when they were placed in water that was too cold when the display tank was first set up.

It was a lot of fun to present the tank reared orchid dottybacks at MACNA VIII. It was just one year ago that I received the tiny pair from Bill, and now just one year later their offspring are going back into the hobby at the same conference.

There are still just two pairs of dottybacks now spawning, the original pair and one of the first three pairs that
were set up last June. The other two pairs are acting like
pairs but have not started spawning. There is the possibility that these pairs are made up of two females each, although one is larger in each pair and occupies the PVC
den that I provided. The spawns are large and still 6 days
apart for the older pair. The younger pair seems to go a bit
longer between spawns, but I don't know for sure since I
haven't kept accurate records of every spawn. It kills me to
turn my back on a tanks full of 1000 new hatched orchid
dottybacks, which happen all too frequently these days (I
know I've mentioned this before), but I just don't have the
time to rear them. This will probably be the last entry, I am
going to really bear down on the Breeding Book from now
on.

Now there is a hurricane brewing in the Caribbean just
below Cuba, Lille is her name, and she is heading our way.
Like I don't have enough problems right now...

11

January 1997 -

Another Try, Another Run

January 2, 1997

HAPPY NEW YEAR! OK, now that the holidays are over, it's time to crank up the orchid dottyback journal once again. I have not attempted another rearing run on *P. fridmani* since late last summer, but now I will make one last run. I cleaned up the 30 gallon brood stock tank that is on the closed breeding system to ready it for pigmy angel brood stock, and while it is cleaned up and waiting, this is a good time to make one more orchid dottyback run. The original pair has a great spawn in brood stock tank 3, despite the pair of *Centropyge argi* andthe pair of ocellaris clowns that also share that tank, and this will be a good spawn to work with. It should hatch on Saturday night, January 4 (or possibly Friday night).

I cleaned out the tank yesterday, added new saltwater, with a little old water from the brood stock system, and started an algal bloom and also added a small rotifer inoculation. It should be ready by Friday or Saturday. I will add the streptomycin on Friday AM and add a little more algae late today or early Friday. I want to have a light algal bloom and fair rotifer population in the tank when the larval dottybacks are introduced.

I started 4 rearing containers for rotifers, two gallon jars, one 2 gallon fish bowl and one 4 gallon pretzel jar with a V8® and yeast base to rear the rotifers that will be necessary. Also reestablished the algae cultures into four gallon jars, which should provide the algae for enrichment of the rotifers before they are fed.

I have made little attempt to set up any more breeding pairs up to this point. Evidently the first pair, formed from the first two juveniles that came through metamorphosis, are both males?, perhaps due to relative isolation ?, although they were always in the same tank together. One of the first pairs that were formed and that began spawning in brood tank 1 are still spawning, but not as regularly as the original pair. Another pair was placed in one of the 8 gallon larval rearing tanks (temporarily) and they have also started to spawn.

I will include the impending run in the 30 gallon tank in this journal. Perhaps I can get over 500 through with the larger tank and the capability for easier water changes. Bill Addison of C-Quest told me yesterday that the most that they have been able to bring through so far of this species in a 300 gallon tank is 560. They are now bringing them through on just brine shrimp, which I would suppose entails very careful feeding to avoid over or under feeding. There may also be a few copepods included with the cultured rotifers. I will try the shrimp bits along with the brine shrimp napulii, and I suppose, some wild plankton also, but I will try to keep this at a minimum. I do have to find a new plankton collection site since they are building a new bridge right over my old site.

January 3, 1997, 3:04 PM

Day 1. Well this is the first day of the 30 gallon run. I wasn't expecting to begin the run until the hatch on the night of the 4th, but I had an unexpected hatch from the young pair in the 8 gallon "larval tank". I had set up pairs in the 8 gallon larval tanks to see if active pairs would form in such small tanks and one certainly has and is now breeding actively. The other three pairs may or may not be good pairs, but they have not started breeding as yet. I transferred the larvae to the 30 gallon tank last night. It was not a large hatch, probably about 300 larvae, but it will supplement the hatch I expect on the 4th. I started feeding rotifers to the 30 gallon tank and although they are a little sparse yet, the larvae are very active and are feeding well in the turbulence that the air release creates.

I have 4 rotifer jar cultures set up and they are producing well so far. I am feeding them a mix of V8® strained though the 500 micron sieve mixed with two teaspoons of bakers yeast. One 340 ml can of V8® is diluted with about 1000 ml of cold fresh water and the yeast is then added and the mixture shaken or stirred till all the yeast is dissolved. This mixture is refrigerated and will hold for a week or two. The rotifers are fed twice a day and about every three days the culture is "refreshed" by sieving out the rotifers and either saving the water, cleaning the sediment out of the container, and reestablishing the culture with a portion of the rotifers, or changing the water completely and restarting the culture with new water and a new feeding of the V8® mix.

8:20 PM

I might not have enough rotifers in the rearing tank. I pulled down one of the rearing containers and fed half the rotifers to the 30 gallon tank and put the other half into an algae/Super Selco enrichment jar. I then fed most of that jar later in the afternoon. The larvae are feeding strongly. I am hesitant to feed extensively since the rotifer cultures are still coming up and the big hatch is still scheduled for tomorrow night. Hopefully the rotifer cultures will be strong on Sunday and I can start a schedule of feeding 80% of a culture jar each day and that way each jar will have 4 days to recover with 20% of the original culture. I will try the shrimp bits feeding when the larvae are about 5 days old. I hope that this will be a good substitute for wild plankton, or at least reduce the need for wild plankton.

January 5, 1997, 1:10 PM

Day 3 (or day 1, depending on which hatch). As anticipated, the spawn of the original pair, a good sized egg ball, hatched last night at about 9:00 PM, a half hour after the tank lights went out. It was not the largest hatch that I have seen this pair produce, but it was a good one. I would estimate about 800 hatchlings. I put this hatch into the 30 gallon tank that was prepared for it, along with the smaller hatch from the pair in the 8 gallon tank. There are probably a little over a thousand larval orchid dottybacks in that tank at this time. All are feeding actively on enriched rotifers. They congregate near the surface, up under the auxiliary light (a mini light with two 9 watt bulbs, one daylight and one actinic) that is placed on the acrylic tank cover.

I was concerned about that tank heating up and checked the temperature this morning, but no fear, it was only at 27.5 degrees C. (Actually winter is the time that I have the most trouble with high temperatures in the fish room. Outside temperatures are often in the 70's to 80's F and the air conditioner does not run too often since the thermostat is in another room and the fish room, actually the fish bathroom, does not receive enough cool air to counteract the effect of the lights and pumps. I know how sorry you must feel for me, as you shovel snow and keep an electric heater on your automobile engine, but I do accept your sympathy.)

The larval fish congregate very densely right in the turbulence of the air column where it spreads out over the surface of the tank. It is quite a sight to see a thousand tiny silver larvae lined up and darting into the turbulence after the rotifers. As they age, they will spread throughout the tank more evenly. The time of greatest rotifer consumption will come in about 5 days. At that time I will have to supplement with the shrimp bits and/or wild plankton.

I fed a good amount of enriched rotifers this morning and this should be enough to keep them going today. The rotifer cultures are coming up strong and it looks like the 4 containers, two gallon glass jars, one 2 gallon glass fish bowl, and the 3 gallon plastic pretzel jar, will produce all the rotifers I will need for this run. The mix of V8® and yeast seems to grow them quite well and I add a drop or two of Super Selco every couple of days to provide some of the necessary fatty acids. The algae cultures are now very weak because I did not have many jars going when I started this run (didn't plan far enough ahead), and I have to depend more on the V8® to condition the rotifers for feeding. I would rather have the micro algae cultures to feed the rotifers for 4 to 6 hours before feeding them to the fish larvae, but I have to go with the V8® at the beginning of this run.

2:00 PM

Checked the rotifer level in the tank with a magnifying glass and they are thinning out. The larvae all have food organisms in the guts. I may have to add some more rotifers toward the end of the day.

January 7, 1997, 7:30 PM

Day 5 (or day 3 for the big hatch). Fed rotifers (V8® and yeast based rotifers) this morning. I have been adding a drop of Super Selco to the rotifer culture containers about once every two days and this way I don't have to enrich the rotifers for a few hours before feeding, especially if I don't have the algae to add to the enrichment mix. I think it is better to use the algae and Super Selco as a final enrichment, but it may not be necessary, especially if wild plankton is used at some point in the rearing process.

I added some new hatch brine shrimp napulii about 6 PM this evening and sure enough, all the dottyback larvae are feeding on them. I will use brine shrimp napulii very sparingly until I can get some wild plankton on them, which should be this Friday, day 8.

There has been some mortality, I can see a few bright spots (eyes) on the bottom, but there are relatively few. These are probably larvae that never began to feed, there are always a few like this in each hatch.

January 8, 1997, 7:20 PM

Day 6 (4). The larvae are doing well, most are feeding on rotifers and quite a few are feeding on a mix of rotifers and brine shrimp napulii. I haven't yet had time to get wild plankton and I probably won't be able to until Friday (day 8) but they should do well until then. The rotifers are accumulating at the surface of the tank more then I have seen them do before. This is probably because the 30 gallon tank is deeper then the other rearing tanks and there is less surface turbulence in this tank. There are still many rotifers spread throughout the water column, however, and the larvae seem to be able to find as many as they want. So far no problems and no significant mortality.

January 10, 1997, 11:30 AM

Day 8 (6). Here it is day 8, day 6 for the large hatch, and I still haven't gotten any wild plankton on this run. They seem to be doing well, however, on the enriched rotifers and a sparse amount of brine shrimp napulii. The rotifers are only enriched now with Super Selco. I have very little algae. Only one jar came up green and that is rather weak. I am sure that there is much contamination in the algae cultures. Until I can reestablish the algae cultures I will have to go with the V8® culture medium. So far it seems to be working well, a great amount of rotifers with relatively little effort. The nutritional value of rotifers reared on this formula, however, has yet to be determined.

The larval dottybacks are scattered throughout the tank at this point. They seem to congregate near the bottom now and don't aggregate in the light and turbulence at the surface. They seem to be growing well, however. I have fed some "shrimp bits" yesterday and today. They seem to be interested, but the bits are still a bit large for them and I doubt that they are feeding actively on them. I think that by day 12 to 15 they should be able to take them very well. I will try to get some wild plankton on them today.

January 11, 1997, 11:20 AM

Day 9 (7). Yesterday I committed my first felony. It was easy, no one caught me. I guess that's one of the terrible things about crime, the first one is easy and after that it's hard to stop until you get caught. One can become addicted to easy wild plankton. It was day 8, time for a shot of wild plankton on the dottyback run. The tides were bad, high tide at about 8:00 AM and 8:00 PM, which meant that to get plankton on the incoming tide I would have to tow at either 5 or 6 AM or 5 or 6 PM, both difficult times. I knew that my "premo" spot for towing plankton was now the construction site for a new bridge, but I didn't have time to scout out a new location. I elected to visit the old site at 6:00 PM, after the workmen had gone for the day, and see if it would be possible to tow a little plankton. The old abutment that jutted out into the tidal flow was still there, in fact it was even better because the seawall had been filled with cement and it was now a nice platform. There were a few temporary barriers along the road way, but there was nothing blocking access to the site—except for a sign, a sign that screamed, "NO TRESPASSING Trespassing is a Felony and Violators will be Prosecuted."

Hmmm... what to do. Commit a felony and get 30 minutes worth of wild plankton, or go searching all over the Broward County waterfront with only the light of a new moon to try to find another towing site? The sea wall was only 15 feet from the sign and not a soul in sight... I succumbed to the siren call of ill gotten riches, walked over to the sea wall and set the plankton net. Ah, the sweetness of illicit plankton, and it was good plankton, cool water very rich with copepods, copepodites, and copepod napulii. Now I don't recommend that you commit felonies to indulge your hobby, remember, Crime Does Not Pay!. I am going to find a new towing site, very soon. But maybe, on Day 12, if the tides are right and no one is looking... No, I will not be tempted again. Oh by the way, don't tell anyone about my lapse into crime. I'm going to try to go straight and never err again.

The dottyback larvae were appreciative of the wild plankton and there was enough in two 15 minute tows with the half meter net for at least 3 days of supplemental feeding. Today they are all well fed and seem to be doing well. However, I did observe some unusual behavior. The larvae no longer aggregate near the surface, preferring to stay close to the bottom and many of them were actually bumping on the bottom in two very small areas. I did not observe anything unusual about these areas, except that one was in a corner and had no sediment or algae growth in that area, and the other was in the center at the back edge of the tank. I moved the air stones and changed the position of the light and most of the larvae then moved up and ceased that seemingly unnatural behavior. There may have been some unusual internal reflection in these areas. However, this also coincided with the introduction of food, more plankton, rotifers, and a little brine shrimp so it is difficult to say what caused the behavior to change.

They seem to be growing well at this point. I will soon have to make another decision. The original pair has produced another large egg ball, which will hatch perhaps tomorrow night. Do I put more larvae in the tank, which had probably the optimum number of larvae at this point, or do I practice what I preach and let the hatch go and not risk over populating the tank. Well we will see what the situation is when the egg ball hatches.

January 12, 1997, 3:15 PM

Day 10 (8). The little larvae are eating everything I throw into the tank, well almost everything. I fed a lot of shrimp bits this morning and observed what I thought to be feeding activity, but I can't confirm it unless I do some very careful dissection of recently fed larvae. Which I may

do at some time, but not today. I am over harvesting a bit
to get enough rotifers for the tank; the gallon jars will produce a lot of rotifers on the V8® /yeast diet, but even that
requires three or four days to build up a dense population
of rotifers. The rotifer cultures are also developing a large
population of ciliates, which may be good for some very
small larvae, but it seems to depress rotifer growth. Starting the cultures over gets rid of the ciliates for about a
week, but they soon come back. Starting over cuts back the
rotifer cultures also, so one probably needs more than 3 or
4 culture jars to adequately support a large run in the middle of the larval stage. I will get some more wild plankton
next Tuesday or Wednesday. I hope they can get by without too much mortality till then.

January 13, 1997, 12:50 PM

Day 11 (9). On schedule, there was another large hatch
of larval orchid dottybacks last night. The 9 to 11 day old
larvae, however, are now quite large and about out of the
rotifer feeding stage. To add another large hatch to that
tank, and I wasn't prepared to set up another larval tank,
would have made it difficult to bring the older larvae
through and very difficult to provide the food to allow the
youngest larvae to survive. So I only added a few, perhaps
100, from the new spawn to the old larval tank. Some of
the new hatch dottyback may survive, but I am not going
to make a real effort to bring them through.

I have also not made a major effort to regain strong micro algae cultures. Only one jar is now coming up and I'm
not sure that it will develop into a good culture. I am rely-
ing entirely on the V8® /yeast, B vitamin nutrient mix for
the rotifer cultures. These rotifers are not better than those
produced in micro algae cultures, probably considerably

less nutritious, but the cultures are certainly more consistent in maintaining large populations of rotifers in a home environment under less then sterile conditions.

I made an interesting observation this morning on these cultures. The V8® provides a vegetable based nutrition for the rotifers and the yeast provides a relatively long suspended food supply for the rotifers. Together, they allow for rapid development of high population densities of rotifers in small containers. However, two important maintenance problems develop in these cultures. First, the V8® and yeast eventually form a flocculent material that clogs the culture and makes it difficult to separate the rotifers from the flock for feeding or enrichment in an algae and/or a Selco solution. And second, the V8® and yeast seem to foster the development of a small ciliate that contaminates the culture and eventually seems to displace the rotifers, or at least they become the most dominant life form in the culture. This ciliate is about one tenth to one quarter the size of a rotifer and could be a food organism itself for a species that requires a very small food organism. They can be cultured in vast quantities with the V8®/yeast method.

I found that I could first let the culture stand without aeration for about 30 minutes, which allows almost all the flock to settle to the bottom. Then by either siphoning or decantation, remove the culture water with the rotifers and ciliates and pass it through a 150 micron sieve. This passage allows all the rotifers and ciliates to pass, but removes almost all the remaining flocculent matter. Then it is possible to achieve almost total separation of the ciliates and rotifers by passing the culture water through a 53 micron sieve. The rotifers are captured above the 53 micron sieve and the ciliates (and the smallest rotifers) pass through it.

Washing the rotifers captured above the sieve with clean saltwater removes any remaining ciliates and clears all the old culture water from the rotifers. The cleaned rotifers can then be used to restart a culture or to feed to larval or filter feeding organisms. Try never to expose the rotifers to air by allowing them to lie exposed on the top of the sieve or by introducing excessive bubbles or foam when poring the cultures through the sieves. Open exposure to air allows the rotifers to include air within their lorica and when this happens they float on the surface of the tank and are not available to the larval fish.

There is a little work involved, but it is a reliable and sure way to produce a vast number of rotifers without the uncertainties of casual algae culture and the rigors of sterile laboratory algal culture technique. The resulting rotifers can be used directly or enriched for several hours in an algae rich and/or Selco solution before feeding. A V8® /yeast culture can go for 3 to 5 days and reach great population densities and then be harvested to half volume, that volume replaced with new saltwater, and the harvesting process repeated in two or three days for several cycles, without the need for complete culture renewal. Feeding is done twice a day with about 50 ml of the V8® /yeast stock solution. Keep the V8® /yeast stock solution under refrigeration.

Total renewal of the culture is relatively easy. First settle and then remove all the culture water with the rotifers and ciliates that may be present. Scrub the culture container, gallon jar or other two or three gallon container. Cultures of greater volume than 3 gallons are more difficult to process but can produce rotifers for longer periods before renewal is required. Then scrub out the containers using an abrasive sponge or plastic open weave scrub pad. Rinse the container well, fill with new saltwater and reinoculate the container with washed rotifers. The larger the inoculation of rotifers, the sooner the rotifer population will become large enough to sustain harvesting and the longer the productive period of the culture before ciliates bloom or organic matter accumulates to the point that renewal is necessary.

I have also found that a light rotifer culture will keep for days, even a week, in a Kordon Breathing Bag ™ with a light feeding of the V8® formula. This will make it very easy to ship starter rotifer cultures anywhere in the world.

January 15, 1997, 4:30 PM

Day 13 (11). Ho Hum, another day, another felony. It's almost too easy. The work on the bridge as been stopped for some reason and no one was on the site. In fact the catwalks are all boarded up and it looks as if there is a hiatus in the work. I may be able to get all the plankton I need at that site for this run before they start work once again. I slipped past the NO TRESPASSING sign and no one bothered me during the tows. It was wet, rainy and cold and making the two 15 minute plankton tows was not fun. Also we have had 8 inches of rain so far this month, most of it in the last week. The salinity was down to 25 ppt, so I wasn't sure how good the plankton would be. The collections were dark, and full of silt, but there was an acceptable level of copepods and the larvae are happy now.

They were looking a bit poorly during the last day, growth seemed to have paused and there were a lot of drifters with empty guts. There has also been more than an acceptable level of mortality and the activity level of the larvae seems not as high as it was in the last run at this point. I don't have as many nor as well nourished rotifers on this run either as the algae cultures have declined. The V8® /yeast method of rearing rotifers has its limitations and it takes a lot of rotifers to keep a 30 gallon tank full of very hungry fish larvae going after day 6 or 7. I have also not done any water changes or bottom cleaning so far this run. With the 30 gallon tank, the volume of water is great enough to allow a bit of leniency in this department. Well, we will see how the run goes. If I get a few hundred through and keep out of jail for trespassing, it will be worthwhile.

January 17, 1997, 3:40 PM

Day 15 (13). There has been a fair amount of mortality in the 30 gallon tank. I can see perhaps 20 dead larvae scattered about the bottom. They are also the larger larvae, which is worrysome. The plankton was not great on the last collection, probably due to the huge rains we had that week. I have been feeding mostly rotifers (not well enriched rotifers, either), brine shrimp napulii, and as of today, a lot of the shrimp bits I make from the frozen shrimp balls that are grated and pushed through the 500 micron sieve. They appeared to be feeding on the shrimp bits rather actively today, they would swim rapidly through the clouds of shrimp bits when I squirted them in with an eye dropper and appeared to be picking up the bits then and for some time after as they drifted in the tank. The guts appeared whitish, which is a good indication that they were ingesting the shrimp, but this is also the color of the liver, so I can't be sure.

I am also feeding the brine shrimp napulii and the guts are an orange color when they are feeding on the brine shrimp, so there is no mistake then. I also changed 3 gallons of water today. The growth at day 15 is not as rapid as this time during the last Great Run. During that run, I made a strong effort to keep a large amount of wild plankton on them as often as possible. I have not been able to do that on this run and I think it is showing up in the reduced growth rate and increased mortality. Whatever happens with this run, it will be interesting to see the results.

Most of the larval fish are staying near the bottom on this run, why I don't know. This makes it difficult to siphon the crud off the bottom since the larvae would also be picked up.

January 21, 1997, 9:15 AM

Day 19 (17). This run has not turned out as well as I had hoped. I was hoping that I could get a large number through in the 30 gallon tank with the capacity for easy water change, and I probably could have if I had put the proper effort into the run. At this point, day 19 or 17, many of the larvae should be almost ready for metamorphosis and at least beginning to pick up the first of the orchid colored chromatophores. Instead, most are small, no color is observable, and mortality is high. Interestingly most of the mortality is occurring in the larger larvae. I have still not yet cleaned the tank bottom, and only one small water change, about 3 gallons was attempted. And even this was not a full change, only a dilution of three gallons.

The cause for this lack of effort on my part is twofold, family problems, my mother is in her last days, which takes up a significant amount of time and and energy from my daily efforts, and I don't have the commitment towards this run as I had in the earlier run. I did get one more plankton run on the larvae last Saturday, day 16, which has brought the larvae through to today. I'm not sure if I will get more plankton today or tomorrow or not, if not, then the run will probably die out or only a few will survive. There are probably about 200 plus in the tank as of now and it is certainly worth it to bring them through. I will evaluate the run again later this morning and make a decision then. It would be a lot easier with clownfish since they do not require the live plankton.

January 22, 1997, 11:00 AM

Day 20 (18). Well it wasn't as bad as I thought. I cleaned the glass, made a real 5 gallon water change and looked carefully. It's amazing how much better you can see in the tank when the algae is scraped off the front glass. There are still over 200 larvae in the tank. Quite a few are over the half inch mark and are beginning to approach metamorphosis. There is still a good bit of mortality, about 10 or 15 per day, and this run will not be nearly as good as the great run of last August, but it is worth taking it through to either disaster or triumph. Triumph in this case being 150 to 200 juveniles. I got wild plankton yesterday afternoon; work on the bridge has resumed, but thankfully it is on the other side of the bridge and I can still slip out on my bulkhead and tow plankton for a half hour or so. I am not the only one that slips past the No Trespassing sign. Whole families fish and play on the seawall among the construction equipment. They don't seem to be at all worried about the felony charge hanging over their heads. The main problem now is fielding the question, "What you catchin?" about every five minutes. I am, of course, occasionally tempted to answer "Oh I'm catching shark excreta, we're studying the decline of the shark populations by quantifying the amount of shark doo in random sampling." But I don't, I don't play with people's minds, honest. Well, maybe once in a while. So far so good.

On another note, I now have what appears to be a *Cryptocaryon* infection in the 55 gallon tank. I only have about 10 orchid dottybacks in that tank, but I can see at least two that have lesions that look like *Cryptocaryon* on them. I will have to break down that tank, remove all the fish, and treat them with a formalin bath and a two or three week copper treatment. More hassles. I know where it came from, I put a flame angel in there that had a spot of crypto and I thought it would be OK since the dottybacks seemed fairly resistant to this parasite. My old boss, Bob Ingle, was very fond of saying, "NEVER ASSUME ANYTHING" and, of course, he was correct.

January 23, 1997, 8:45 PM

Day 21 (19). The remaining larvae, about 200, my guess, seem to be doing well. They are in the late larval stage now, or at least most of them, and they seem vigorous. There are still mortalities every day, but not as many. They feed on the shrimp bits, wild plankton, and brine shrimp. I guess I should stop the wild plankton and go with just the shrimp bits and the brine shrimp napulii just to see if any make it through from this point without the wild plankton, but after this much effort, I want to get at least a few through and I hate to take the chance that none will come through. I won't be able to get plankton again till Saturday or Sunday (Super Bowl Sunday, sure I'll be out there towing plankton, all right). Well I guess it will have to be Saturday.

January 27, 1997, 1:45 PM

Day 25 (23). Here it is 4 days later and I still haven't been out for plankton. There were many problems unassociated with fish, and I just couldn't make the time to get

the plankton. I have been keeping the larvae going with
shrimp bits, some finely particulate flake food and of
course brine shrimp napulii. I have started to enrich the
brine shrimp napulii with Super Selco at this point and I
don't think I will get any more wild plankton for this run.
There are about, oh I would guess 75 or so larvae left and
they are mostly the fast growing large, late stage larvae at
this point. Most of the really rapidly growing larvae, interestingly enough, and the smaller slowest growing larvae
have not survived. I added some bottom substrate to the
tank today, a variety of PVC pipe sections and fittings all
strung together with nylon twine like a loose string of
pearls. This works quite well as it supplies many hiding
places and a dense network of substrate, yet it can be easily removed from the tank and the juvenile dottybacks cannot "hole up" in the PVC as they can do in porous rocks.

   With luck I will get 50 or more juveniles out of this run.
I had hoped to do better, but I could not put in the time
and effort on the run as I did in the larval rearing of last
July and August. It takes a good water quality environment, the additions of micro algae culture seem to help
markedly in this area, and a constant presence of the right
nutritionally adequate food organisms. They can clean a
tank out of food organisms in only a few hours. A good
dose of plankton serves to maintain an adequate food base
longer than brine shrimp napulii. Enriched rotifers are
good, in many ways better than plankton for the first 4 to 6
days (the levels of the proper sized food organisms are easier to maintain with rotifers), but when the larvae get
larger and on days 6 to 12, the rotifers become either too
small, or not nutritious enough, to sustain the dottyback
larvae.

I think the "shrimp bits" are also helpful in this regard, but even though the larvae appear to take them, they settle from the water within 15 to 30 minutes, and are not useful as a major food item since repeated and extensive feeding will foul the water within a day. Some of the available larval feeds may be useful here also, but I have not tried them yet.

I will now hope that these larvae will survive through metamorphosis without more wild plankton, and try to sustain them with the foods I have on hand since I have to get on with writing at this point. I may try another run later in the spring if the book is going well and if I want to have some more juveniles for the conferences coming up in summer and fall. Who knows, maybe by then the pigmy angels will have spawned.

January 29, 1997, 9:15 AM

Day 27 (25). Mortality has leveled off, now a dead larva is unusual. There aren't a great many left now, however, probably only about 50 will make it through the larval stage. I did not get more plankton over the week end. It has now been 7 days since I got plankton. I haven't seen any complete metamorphosis yet, but many of the larvae are showing the reddish hue of pre metamorphic fish. They haven't taken up bottom life yet, at least I haven't seen any taking up residence in the PVC pipe bits and fittings that I placed on the bottom. They should in a few days, however. I started a trickle change on the tank. I can do that since this tank is on the system. It makes taking care of the tank much easier.

If I had a few hundred larvae left, I would probably get more plankton, but with less then 75, I will rely on the enriched brine shrimp and shrimp bits for the rest of the run.

Maybe next spring, if I have the time, I will make another dottyback rearing run. Or if I am working with the pigmy angels and have extra plankton, I may also try it again. We'll see....

January 30, 1997, 1:30 PM

Day 28 (26). Noted about 3 dead larvae today. I'm feeding almost exclusively enriched brine shrimp napulii over the last couple of days. I'll get some shrimp bits on them today. Metamorphosis is quite advanced for most of the larvae and I saw a couple of early juveniles on the sides in the corners and in the PVC pile. I should add a couple of rocks to the tank, although if the rocks have holes then the juveniles are most difficult to remove. The largest fastest growing larvae metamorphosed at about day 27, which is slower than the last run by about 5 days, if I remember correctly. Feeding has been much more sporadic on this run with much less wild plankton and less control of water quality. All in all, I'm happy that some of them made it through and there should be more as the remaining larvae either metamorphose or die.

12

February 1997 -
A Good Try

February 3, 1997, 11:50 AM
Day 32 (30). The 30 gallon tank is now almost a bottom tank rather than a pelagic tank. I have added some PVC pipe structures to go along with the small chain of PVC fixtures and some *Caulerpa* and the leafy red *Halymenia floridana* which the juveniles seem to like. There are about 20 or so juveniles and maybe the same number of late stage larvae that have not yet metamorphosed. There seems to be some resistence in the late larvae to metamorphosis. I don't know if it is just that they are from the later spawn or if the lack of wild plankton over the last week has created a nutritional deficiency. I am feeding only enriched brine shrimp and shrimp bits at this point. We will see how they progress. I can't give them a lot of attention right now because my mother is in hospice and will probably die this week. She is 90 and has had a long full life. It is still a very difficult time, however.

February 5, 1997, 5:00 PM
Day 33, (31). Mom died yesterday, Feb. 4, 1997, at the age of 90 years and 7 months. I am sad and reflective at

this time. I don't really feel that Mom's exit is a tragedy, more of a welcome relief after a few difficult last years, a gentle entry into a deep sleep at the end of a long life. I don't understand life and death, I doubt that anyone really does understand it, but I know that there is joy at the beginning and sadness at the end. I guess now I'm finally a grownup and the last phase of life begins.

The dottybacks are doing well, mortality is nil, but there are still quite a few, perhaps 20 that are still in the late larval stage. Most are juveniles and they are swimming into and about the PVC bottom structures and doing their little orchid dottyback things. I am feeding enriched brine shrimp napulii and the little shrimp bits. For the most part I think that they are through the difficult larval stage and should probably do well up into the late juvenile - early adult stage. I think I will probably get about 50 through in this run. Not nearly as well as I wanted to do, but OK I guess considering the difficulties in giving the run proper attention and nutrition. For all practical purposes, however, this larval run is now over. I will continue the journal on this run if anything exceptional happens. I may do another run later in the spring or early summer if time allows. As for now, back to the Breeding Book, and the intense effort it will take to get it finished by May....

13

March 1997 -
The Journey Ends

March 21, 1997, 11:30 AM

Day 78. Because of the press of other business and projects, I have been neglecting the orchid dottybacks. I left the last hatch in the 30 gallon tank in which they were reared until yesterday. They had developed a parasitic protozoan infection which had destroyed a number of them. It was an unusual type of parasite, it didn't affect other species of fish very much, I think it is a very small strain of *Amyloodinium.* Although I did not see the characteristic white, dust like specks on the external surfaces of the fish, I did see white lesions, usually at the mid point of the dorsal fish and at the nape, just behind the head. Then, as the infection progresses, the tail becomes shredded and necrotic, the pelvic fins also become affected, and the thin white lines that develop on the mid point of the body expand and deepen. The infection seems to enter the musculature at that point and the fish seldom recover after this point is reached.

Treatment with copper and/or formalin, at double the normal treatment dose, (two commercial products I have tried are Organicure, from Aquarium Products Inc. or Sea

Cure from Aquarium Systems) effects a cure and the fins
regenerate, so I am "sure" that the causative agent is a protozoan parasite rather than a fungus or a bacteria.

I examined a moribund fish under the dissecting scope
and then scrapings of the lesions under the compound
scope at 100 and 400 power. I did not see the typical 50 micron or so long ciliate tomites scarfing up cellular debris,
nor the enlarged 200 to 500 micron trophonts, as one usually sees in *Cryptocaryon* or *Brooklynella* infections. But I did
see very small, 10 microns or less, non motile, starch filled
cells (no groove or flagella) that are found in *Amyloodinium*
infections. I found these cells in the cellular debris that
came from scrapings of the infected area on the body and
from the tattered fins on the moribund (near death) small
dottyback that I examined. So without more extensive
analysis, I am tentatively, very tentatively, chalking this up
to *Amyloodinium* and I will have to watch for this strain in
the future. It does not seem to be particularly infectious to
other species, and it does not quickly wipe out a tank of orchid dottybacks, but it does slowly decimate the dottybacks in the tank. I pulled out 30 orchid dottybacks from
this larval/rearing tank and put them in a treatment tank. I
had previously isolated this tank from the system and
treated it with copper, which seemed to slow down the infection, but did not totally eliminate it as the copper/for-
malin treatment did. I suspect that I lost about 10 of the
small juvenile dottybacks to this infection over the last 20
days or so.

I should note that I have very few of the orchid dottyback left from the breeding of last year. They were very
hardy and most of them entered the hobby in some way. A
wholesaler, Sea Critters, from the Tampa area sold many of
them and the remainder were either sold locally or given

to friends. I still have perhaps 50 remaining and I will try to set up a number of pairs to keep a brood stock as long as I can. This will probably be the end of the orchid dottyback journal as I am now beginning to shift my experimental rearing over to pygmy angels, and I also have to put much more effort into the breeding book from now on.

March 26, 1997, 12:25 PM

A final note. The 29 dottybacks (less the one that I dissected) that were moved from the 30 gallon tank and into the treatment tank are doing well. As far as I can tell, there has been no further mortality—the signs of infection have diminished and fins and scales are regenerating. I will keep them under treatment for another week or so and then move them to a natural grow-out tank. The growth of this group has been slower than previous hatches, most likely because I gave them less care and food, and their tank environment was not as good as in previous hatches. This is, for sure, the final entry in the orchid dottyback journal. We have decided to temporarily stop work on the breeding book and prepare the dottyback journal for publication. This way we can get a book out more quickly, and there will be less time between the work and the publication of the information on rearing the dottybacks.

April 9, 1997, 3:10 PM

This is the absolutely last entry in the orchid dottyback journal! Just to wrap things up I should report that the treatment given to the dottybacks has been successful. All but two have survived in the treatment tanks. I am using the 8 gallon larval tanks, filled halfway, for treatment, since this is a more manageable volume. I will move them to a larger tank after three weeks of treatment.

After 15 months of spawning almost every 6 days, like clockwork, the original pair of *Pseudochromis fridmani* has stopped spawning. The male still courts the female and tries to get her to enter his den, but the female does not respond. Her abdomen no longer expands with eggs. I don't know if her reproductive period has ended and she is entering senescence or if this is just a hiatus in her reproductively active life. Come to think of it, it has been a couple of weeks since I have noticed eggs in the dens of the other two spawning pairs, so it may be that I need to pay more attention to the water quality and nutrition of the spawning fish than I have done lately. With breeding fish, you have to stay on top of things all the time, but dottybacks are hardy fish, breed readily, and are not that difficult to rear, certainly more difficult than clownfish or gobies, but much easier than marine angelfish. And with this bit of wisdom, my dottyback journal is closed.

April 23, 1997, 12:20 PM

This absolutely, positively, for sure, the last entry in the dottyback journal. This is a very persistent protozoan infection that the dottybacks have developed. I can keep them under copper for weeks with apparent total remission of the infection, only to have it bounce back when the copper treatment is removed. At this point, I don't have a good identification of the disease causing organism. I will have to look into it at greater depth.

The original pair of *Pseudochromis fridmani* have spawned again, as have at least one pair of their offspring. For a time my interests were diverted from fish care and I'm afraid that feeding suffered in quality and quantity, and water quality also went down in the breeding system. Although I hate to admit it, for a while there I couldn't even see into the tanks because of the algae growth on the inside of the front glass. Don't tell anyone about this. However, as soon as I improved feeding and water quality, the pairs began to spawn once again. So at least the spawning life of the orchid dottyback in captivity is longer than one year. And finally, the dottyback journal is ended.

May 2, 1997, 10:55 PM

OK, this is for sure the last entry. Absolutely for sure. I'm almost done with the Appendix for this book, and then the index and the final edit, the layout, and the cover, and it's off to the printer. But anyway, I brought 7 fish down to Tom Capo at the at the University of Miami RSMAS Aplysia Resource Facility, one nearly adult pair and 5 juveniles. He is going to try to get a marine fish rearing project for students in operation this summer. This will be a good way to continue the development of this technology and keep the species in production, at least in more than one hatchery. I still have three spawning pairs so I can also provide some larvae from time to time.

I talked to Bill Addison at C-Quest last night and he has been rearing many different species of *Pseudochromis*. He mentioned that *P. fridmani* is a relatively difficult species to culture, although I have found them to be very hardy when the minimal environmental and nutritional requirements are met, and also very interesting, he mentioned that *P. olivaceus* is perhaps the least difficult of the *Pseudochromis* to rear. I believe that he used the term "easier than falling off a log" to describe the ease of culture. So for aquarist breeders with a bent toward the basslets, *Pseudochromis* is a good genus to work with, and the attractive green with blue dots *P. olivaceus* may be one of the easiest of them to rear. This species may not need as much wild plankton as *P. fridmani*, and may even be reared only on rotifers and brine shrimp.

Marine fish culture requires time, investment, determination, persistence, innovation, and just plain hard work, and when it comes to rearing marine fish in the 90's, Bill Addison is "The Man". Sure, Frank, Chris, Forrest, Tom, Godfrey, Joe, Sally, Morgan, John, Mike, Joyce, Syd, Fernando, Robert, Paul, Stan, Bill, Todd, Jackie, Kurt, Dave, Connie, and many others, including myself, have reared a lot of fish, but Bill is looking back over his shoulder at all the rest of us.

June 7, 1997, 1:38 PM

(This isn't exactly an entry in the dottyback journal. It's just sort of a last note to wrap things up as the book goes to press, so it doesn't count as the last entry. The previous absolutely for sure, last entry, is still, technically, the final entry in the journal.)

The last run, the winter rearing run, of the orchid dottybacks resulted in about 35 good juveniles (a wonder considering how little attention I paid to this group over the last couple of months). The protozoan infection is still with some of these dottybacks, it is quite persistent, although copper and formalin seems to keep it in check and does seem to eliminate it from most of the fish. But it does require long and careful treatment.

The pair I gave to Tom Capo at the University of Miami has spawned twice so far and they now have larvae in the 6th day. I expect them to bring some of these through the larval stage and into spawning adults. Tom and Byron came up a couple of days ago and I gave them another two pair to augment their spawning stock. As an established university hatchery they should be able to rear these in true scientific fashion and publish the results, which will certainly benefit the industry and the hobby.

My original pair are still spawning regularly, 17 months now, although they have slowed down a bit lately. I set up four pairs of their offspring to keep in a spawning environment and extend the brood stock in case I ever want to do another rearing run. One pair, in a well established 20 gallon brood stock tank, spawns regularly. The other pair in a small 8 gallon tank (a modified larval rearing tank) also spawns, but not as regularly. As of today, I have three spawns in various stages of development. I will try to give the hatchlings to Tom. They can use the practice.

I recently discovered that it is not wise to set up a spawning pair in a small tank. The 8 gallon larval rearing tank (12 x 14 inches) has only 168 square inches of bottom area and this evidently does not allow for quite enough environmental separation between male and female. I thought that the pair were doing well in the small tank since they had been in such close quarters for many months and were spawning frequently. The male actively defends his den from all other dottybacks, including the female, after spawning occurs. He attacks and chases other fish from his territory and, although the male and female can coexist and even spawn with some regularity in such close quarters, the male may occasionally inflict some minor injury on the female. In this case, the female's abdomen was rather soft because of distention from the development of the gonads and the male's attack resulted in a rupture of the abdominal wall. Thus the female died, her gonads full of ripe eggs, and another lesson learned.

The other pair turned out to be two males, why this happened, I don't know, and I eventually had to separate them. These were the first two orchid dottybacks that survived through the larval stage. I kept them together in the small 8 gallon larval rearing tank until they were about 40 days old and then moved them to a 20 gallon brood stock tank. I thought that they would become male and female, but there may have been enough social and environmental separation between them during the time that they became reproductively mature that they both became males. There was also an absence of other fish in the tank during this time, which may also have contributed to their relative isolation. The orchid dottybacks would be an excellent species to use to study the effects of the social environment on the development of sexuality in fish. They can be obtained as very young tank reared juveniles from C-Quest, and they grow rapidly into adults in relatively small tanks.

I am still keeping a good stock of rotifers in a few jars on the V8® formula. Not enough to provide a larval rearing run, but more than enough to maintain holding population. I feed them once a day and change the water about every 10 days, and it is a very easy way to keep a residual population. After about 5 to 6 days the jars are chock full of rotifers and then the populations decline until I reestablish them and then they bloom again. I keep at least two jars, usually three, so that if something happens and one jar crashes, I still have at least one other population.

The cherubfish, *Centropyge argi*, spawn about 200 eggs every night. The midnight pygmy angels, *C. nox*; the flame angels, *C. loriculus*; and the rusty angels, *C. ferrugatus*, have not yet started to spawn, but I think they may start soon. I have not yet started the pygmy angel project. This will be a difficult rearing project, I'm sure, just from the preliminary work I have done with *C. argi*, so I want to have the decks clear before I seriously start that project. I'll keep a journal, however, so you'll be able to find out what happened.

Appendix

Formulas and Techniques

There are a number of techniques and procedures that I have found useful in the home culture of the orchid dottyback. The derivation of these methods is detailed in the day to day entries in the journal, and those accounts will provide some insight into how and why I did things a certain way and how particular techniques developed. Sometimes the stimulus was saving time, or a lack of a particular piece of equipment, or, often, just a more efficient (OK, lazier) way of getting something done. I have detailed some of the more useful of these techniques in this appendix so that you won't have to wear out the index or plow through the journal entries too often.

Rearing Rotifers, The V8® culture method

Rotifers are pretty straightforward creatures. Give them something to eat, a little clean water (and it really doesn't have to be very clean), a little light, absence of predators and competitors, and they will reproduce like tribbles. (Which means that you'll have millions of them of in a week or two.) There are two very important considerations, however. First of all, the rotifers that are fed to the larval fish must be nutritious enough to sustain normal growth and development of the larvae, and second, the rotifers must be abundant enough to provide all the required nutrition for however many larvae are cultured for at least the first 10 days of larval growth. By far, the best way to do this is to feed the rotifers an abundant culture of a nutritious, small celled micro algae. This, however, requires that the breeder maintain a pure culture of one or more of several algae, such as *Nannochlorop-sis, Chlorella, Dunaliella, Monochrysis, Tetraselmis, Isochrysis, T-Isochrysis*, etc...., or if you haven't the time or equipment to maintain sterile cultures, just a growth of "green water" (which, without great care, is what you will probably wind up with anyway), and then also culture these algae in large enough quantities to feed the voracious rotifers day in and day out, until they themselves are food for larval fish. Done correctly, this type of algae culture requires careful fertiliza-tion, usually with some form of Guillard's F/2 type fertilizer media, sterile culture containers, daily maintenance of cul-tures, and due care to prevent contamination of the algae cultures with stray rotifers, ciliates, and/or blue green algae. Done correctly, this can be a full time job all in itself.

I had problems with algae culture. I first worked with a wild strain of *Chlorella*, which made a beautiful bloom in the 50 gallon grow-out tank for several months, but it eventually died out, and then *T-Isochrysis* and then *Nannochloropsis*, all of which grew first rate rotifers. (In fact, at one point I had 50 gallons of first rate rotifers, which was one reason that the *Chlorella* died out.) However, I did not keep properly sterile culture containers or sterilize the algae culture water or maintain the cultures on a proper schedule.

One can easily sterilize algae culture water with a few minutes in a microwave oven, but I didn't do this. And I did not keep the cultures under constant lighting, which may, or may not, increase the tendency of the algae to plate out on the jar surfaces. As a result, my algae cultures kept crashing or plating out and I had problems producing enough rotifers at precisely the time that I needed them the most. The solu-tion that worked for me about halfway through the project was to set up a large volume (30 gallon), outside rotifer culture, feed yeast to keep it going and produce a good rotifer population, harvest this culture to supplement the inside cultures when needed, and then fortify these rotifers with several hours of feeding them in a small container filled with algae and an omega-3 fatty acid supplement. The resulting rotifers were nutritious enough to support the fish larvae for at least 6 to 8 days with relatively little mortality. But I still had the problems of algae culture, although these problems, and the required culture maintenance, were much reduced since much less algae was required.

There must be, I thought, as I was having a typical lunch one day of a sandwich and a can of V8® vegetable juice, an inexpensive, adequate substitute for micro algae that will grow nutritious rotifers out there somewhere. And the little light bulb went off as I drank the vegetable juice. Why not, I thought, it's worth a try. I experimented with the V8® juice and found that after introduction of the V8® into a rotifer culture, all their little guts turned red, and the next day there were many, many eggs hanging off almost every little rotifer.

The V8® method is not a panacea, there were and are problems, but then this is a nascent technique (Nascent means something that is new, budding, just beginning, or possibly something you might find in your nose. Take your choice.) and there is much to yet prove out and to develop. I found that the V8® produces a lot of flocculent material in the culture water, settles out rather rapidly, and stimulates any ciliates in the culture to really bloom. These problems can be dealt with, however. The following formula details the preparation and feeding of my V8® rotifer culture formula, as I now use it.

Preparing the rotifer feeding formula

1. Take one 11.5 oz. (340 ml) can of V8® juice (I suppose any brand of vegetable juice would be acceptable) and strain it through a 500 micron sieve. Typical window screening is 1000 microns and those little stainless steel strainers you can buy in the supermarket are about 500 microns. This straining removes the larger particles that do not help the culture.

2. Dilute the strained juice with about one quart (950 ml) of cold fresh water. It is easier to strain the juice if it is diluted first or during the straining process.

3. Add two teaspoons of bakers yeast. The yeast is optional, it is mainly a feeding supplement to the juice particles, but I find that the culture is more stable in that food remains in suspension longer and this helps the rotifers maintain high population levels, and reduces the need for more frequent feedings. The amount, or even the use of yeast is a subject for future experimentation.

4. I then add several drops of an omega-3 fatty acid supplement (Super Selco, another type of fish food supplement or even an Omega-3 or fish oil supplement from a health food store) to the V8® solution and also add a pre dissolved B vitamin complex tablet and a vitamin C tablet. Put the top tightly on the container and shake very well. It may well be that different supplements or different amounts of these supplements will produce a better rotifer food. Much experimentation remains to be done.

This mixture is then kept in the refrigerator and a portion is fed to the rotifer cultures each day in an amount fitting to the purpose of the culture. I feed about 30 to 50 ml per day to each gallon jar of rotifers to maintain rotifer populations at low levels during periods between breeding projects. High production would require at least two, perhaps three similar feedings each day. Stir the formula well before feeding.

Processing rotifers for feeding

The vegetable particles in the juice coalesce and form a flock that drifts in the culture and accumulates on the bottom of the culture vessel. Rotifers feed on and in this flock as well on the microscopic vegetable and yeast particles that are in suspension. When rotifers are harvested, this flock can be reduced in two ways. First, remove the air release in the culture, allow the flock to settle for 15 minutes or so, and then siphon off the rotifers that are suspended in the water column. Second, after settling, pass the rotifers and the collected water through a 150 micron sieve. A sieve of this mesh size passes all the rotifers through, but retains most of the flock, which can then be washed out of the sieve. The water can be returned to the rotifer culture or disposed of, depending its age and condition. The rotifers can then be collected on top of a 53 micron mesh sieve, or 35 microns if the very smallest rotifers are desired. When siphoning and sieving rotifers, it is very important that the rotifers are never exposed "dry" on the bottom of the sieve. If this occurs, many of the rotifers will ingest an air bubble into their lorica (the outer shell), will float on the surface, and will not be available to the larvae.

Although I have done it often, rotifer culture water should not be added to the larval tank, for this adds unnecessary bacteria and organic compounds to the larval culture water.

Maintenance of rotifer cultures

There are three problems that develop, or can develop, in this method of rotifer culture that require attention. These are degradation of water quality, accumulation of flock, and, possibly, ciliate contamination of the culture. With small cultures, one to five gallons, it is a relatively simple matter to change the water and clean the culture vessel. First allow the flock to settle, then harvest the rotifers as above, and place them in clean water in another culture vessel. Jars and trays can be easily cleaned with tap water and an abrasive sponge. They can be rinsed with a chlorine solution or even allowed to stand a day or so with a chlorine solution if sterilization is desired. Usually, at least for just maintenance of cultures, I clean the vessel well and then replace the rotifers into clean water in the same culture vessel.

It takes a while, several days to a week or so, for a small innoculum of rotifers to reach a decent population level. The more rotifers that are used to start a new culture, the less time it will take for the populations to reach harvestable levels. Depending on the age and condition of the culture, harvesting can consist of removal of a portion of the population, with return of the water or replacement with new water, and continued feeding to that culture, or total harvest of that culture and establishment of a new culture with a portion of the harvested rotifers.

Another problem that may develop in both algae fed rotifer cultures and V8® formula fed cultures is ciliate infestation of the culture. A ciliate about one tenth the size of a rotifer and possibly a second species that is a little smaller, can populate these cultures in vast numbers and eventually eliminate the rotifers in the culture. (I haven't an identification of these little beasties yet, and probably there are many species that can develop in these cultures, so identification of one of these may not be very helpful.) I have seen these ciliates cleaning out the inside of the lorica (the outer "shell") of rotifers, but I don't know if they attacked and killed the rotifer, or are just scavenging. I have had cultures go for many days, weeks, with both ciliates and rotifers coexisting, so I suspect scavenging rather then predation. Certainly, competition for food exists and the ciliates can probably reproduce more quickly and overwhelm rotifer populations even if they do not kill rotifers directly. These ciliates feed extensively on the flock that forms in the V8® cultures.

It is certainly possible to maintain ciliate free, rotifer cultures, all that needs to be done is to avoid adding ciliates to new or renewed cultures, which is a bit difficult to achieve once they have penetrated the culture system. I have been able to almost eliminate ciliates from V8® rotifer cultures by mechanical sieving. The trick is to pass the rotifer culture through a 53 micron sieve. Rotifers are captured on top of the sieve, while ciliates pass through the sieve. Rinsing the rotifers in the sieve very well with new, uncontaminated saltwater several times serves to wash out residual ciliates, and while this process may not totally eliminate ciliates from the new rotifer culture, it lowers the ciliate population to the point that a highly productive rotifer culture can be attained and harvested before the ciliates regain strong population levels. Ciliates may enter the cultures along with the starter rotifer innoculum or through sea water or from unsterile algae cultures. Ciliate free cultures could probably be achieved by first repeated sieving, and then by starting a new, clean culture from a small quantity of rotifers taken from an apparently ciliate free aliquot from that repeatedly sieved culture.

I also tried chemical separation of rotifers and ciliates with copper and formalin, hoping that the ciliates might be less resistant to these treatments, and die out while the rotifers would survive longer and could then be transferred to a new, ciliate free culture medium. No luck, the ciliates outlasted the rotifers.

These ciliates are interesting little creatures, however, and I am reluctant to totally eliminate them from these maintenance cultures because they may have possibilities. They are very much smaller than rotifers, but the largest of them is not too small to possibly be taken by very small fish larvae. Their movement is somewhere in between the jerky motion of copepod napulii and the smooth, flowing movement of rotifers. These larger ciliates, reared in a culture medium rich in omega-3 fatty acids, might work for rearing very small fish larvae to the point where they can take rotifers, wild plankton, or even brine shrimp napulii. This is certainly something to experiment with and I have intentions.....

Without supplemental algae feeding, I'm not sure that the rotifers that result from the V8® culture method will be properly nutritious for all species of larval fish, but the method lends itself to great modifications in composition, feeding amounts and culture techniques, so one may be able to adapt it to any specific circumstance. It is wise to maintain at least three separate cultures of rotifers to prevent total loss due to accident or contamination. The V8® method most probably does not produce a better rotifer for larval feeding than algae cultures, and, in the long run, may not be that much less labor intensive than a well thought out, carefully implemented, algae culture regimen, but I have found that it is a sure way to maintain rotifer cultures without the uncertainties of micro algae culture, and a much easier way to keep a small population of rotifers going between rearing projects.

One and two gallon V8® rotifer cultures about one week old and in need of reestablishment

As a last note on the rotifer, *Brachionus plicatilis*, that is most used in aquatic marine culture, I should mention that these little creatures have a complex life cycle that includes sexual and asexual stages. To culture the vast numbers of rotifers that are required for larval food, rotifers are propagated in the asexual stage. Changing food, temperature, salinity and other environmental and genetic factors may shift reproduction to the sexual stage, and the egg (cyst) that is produced as a product of sexual interaction is thick walled and capable of a long dormancy and even dessication. If a culture crashes and no living rotifers are seen, it does not necessarily mean that the culture is dead. Some sexual cysts may have been produced and may be present in the detritus on the bottom of the culture. I have resurrected cultures from time to time by placing recovered detritus into a new culture situation or even by changing water in an old culture vessel without cleaning the bottom. The Plankton Culture Manual by Hoff and Snell (1993) provides extensive information on algae and rotifer culture, and Moe (1989, 1992) also provides information on algae and rotifer culture. My marine tropical fish breeding book, now in prepartation will also have extensive information on plankton/rotifer culture.

Larval recovery methods

In a commercial operation, when it is important to recover almost all the hatched larvae and where it is often inconvenient and time consuming to collect larvae at night, it is customary to remove the nests of demersal spawners such as clownfish and gobies a few hours before the scheduled hatch and incubate the eggs in the rearing tank until hatch, or as in the case of neon gobies, hatch the eggs manually. Hatching usually happens in the untended tank and the larvae are there waiting for food the next morning. I suppose that dottyback egg balls could be removed a few hours before hatch and set up to hatch automatically in the rearing tank, but I'm not sure that this would be successful because of the great agitation that the male gives to the egg ball at the time of larval hatch. He wrestles with it, bites and shakes it, and spins his body and fins around it. This stimulation may be necessary for the eggs to hatch and it would be difficult to put together an automatic device that would supply just the right amount of agitation that is necessary.

For my purposes, however, and probably for most home aquarists, it is not necessary to recover every last larvae from every spawn just for experimental and hobbyist breeding programs. Hatching in the orchid dottyback, and most other demersal spawning species that I have worked with, almost always takes place within an hour or two after the lights have gone out. This makes it relatively easy, if you live in same in house as your fish, to set up the tank so that the larvae are not flushed out of the tank immediately after hatch, and so that you can concentrate the larvae in one small area of the tank and remove all that you need for rearing with a either a siphon or by collecting them in a cup or glass.

This larval recovery procedure works well with the dottybacks and also with clownfish. First turn off all the water flow in the tank, filters, air lifts, power heads, etc. This won't hurt the fish and invertebrates in the tank as long as you remember to turn it all back on in a couple of hours after the larvae have been harvested. Then just after hatching, mount a flashlight or other relatively concentrated, not too bright light source over one corner of the tank. Allow 10 to 15 minutes for the larvae to concentrate under the light source and then remove them by siphon or by dipping them out with a cup or glass. I have found that siphoning into a bucket (make sure that there is an inch or two of water already in the bottom of the bucket) is the most efficient method and as far as I can tell, the larvae survive the passage through the siphon very well.

Rotifer and plankton sorting methods

It is imperative that rotifers and plankton be sorted through sieves before feeding to the larval rearing tank. Sorting removes organisms too large for the early stage larvae and many of the predators in wild plankton collections, and reduces the amount of culture water and wild sea water that enters the larval rearing tanks. There are some ready made plankton sorters waiting for you at the local supermarket. Just ask the stockboy where the plankton sorters are and he will unhesitatingly point you toward aisle eleven. Yeah, right. However, if you look in housewares at all the various stainless steel and nylon strainers for tea, spaghetti, pasta, coffee and what all else that are hanging there next to the spatulas and cookie cutters, you might well find some strainers that will be helpful. Ordinary window screen is about 1000 microns and this is about the size of the largest mesh supermarket mesh strainers. A mesh this size comes in handy once in a while, especially for wild plankton, but the smaller mesh sizes are more useful.

Probably the smallest mesh size one can find in a housewares department will be about 400 microns, a little less than half the size of window screen. Metal coffee filters are smaller, sometimes down to almost 100 microns, but they are often awkward to use and clean, and the coffee tastes funny afterward. The most useful supermarket strainers are the stainless steel mesh strainers that are of the right size to fit on top of a measuring cup or a glass and are about 400 to 500 microns in mesh size.

To work with rotifers and wild plankton, however, you have to get down to the 50 micron range, and for sorting and concentrating really small organisms, such as ciliates, a 10 or 20 to 30 micron mesh is required. I have sorters that are 53 microns, 150 microns, 250 microns, about 500 microns and then 700 and 1000 microns, and these sizes do almost everything I need for clownfish and dottyback culture. For my next project, the pigmy angels, I will have to get some sieves in the 10 to 30 micron range.

Synthetic nylon screening and stainless steel screening is available from most scientific supply and aquaculture supply mail order houses. It usually comes in lengths of one running yard, about 10 square feet for the nylon screening, and the usual minimum purchase of the stainless steel screening is a running foot length off a four foot wide roll of screening. The nylon screening comes in various mesh sizes

A variety of sieves and strainers used for sorting plankton and rotifers.

from 35 to 1000 microns and the stainless steel from 500 to 1000 microns. Prices range from $15 to $50 a yard for the nylon screening and $15 to $20 a foot for the stainless steel screening. The nylon screening is pretty much of a "must have" for rotifer and plankton sorting, but the supermarket stainless mesh strainers can do quite well unless you need a large surface area of stainless steel mesh.

I use nylon screening in sizes of 53, 150, 250, microns and PVC window screen at about 1000 microns. The stainless steel mesh strainers that I got at the supermarket are about 500 microns. I make up strainers with the nylon mesh cloth by getting plastic containers with plastic tops in sizes varying from a few ounces to a quart. The center of the plastic top is cut out leaving the rim and only about a half inch of the top, and the bottom of the container is also cut off. The nylon screening is lightly stretched over the open top of the container and the lid, with the center cut out, is screwed tightly onto the container. Excess screening is cut off around the edge of the lid, and when the device is turned over, you have a sieve with a nylon mesh bottom that can hold ounces to pints and is a very efficient strainer to whatever mesh size is under the cut out top. In use, the smaller the mesh size the more quickly it will clog and the slower the flow through the strainer. Flow through small mesh sizes can be enhanced by patting and rubbing the underside of the mesh while pouring the rotifer culture into the container. Again, be careful not to totally empty the sieve and expose the rotifers on the mesh bottom of the sieve. If you do so, the rotifers will pick up air in their lorica, float on the surface of the larval rearing tank, and not be available to the larval fish or invertebrates.

"Through the glass" larval observation technique

It is very important to know what the fish larvae are doing, especially in the early days of development. Things to try to determine are whether on not they are actually feeding, what is the density of the rotifer population in the tank (are all those little white dots in the tank rotifers, copepods, or just planktonic detritus), are the larval guts full, partly full, or empty , are there parasites on some of the larvae, are some of the larvae deformed, what is the population density of the food organisms throughout the day, and other determinations that require close observations to answer. The typical method is to take a sample of tank water and a larva or two and examine these samples under a dissecting microscope or a high power hand lens. One of those neat little 10 to 15 x lenses used to examine 35 mm slides works rather well in this application. And although this is important to do, once a little experience is gained, it is possible to get most of this information more quickly and easily with a hand lens held close to the front glass.

Sometimes, if you observe the tank this way, things might seem blurred, dark and indistinct. Usually, cleaning the algae off the inside of the glass clears this up in a hurry. A powerful hand lens, 10 power or more, gives you a very short depth of focus that is quite close to the inside of the glass. This is valuable for determining the condition of the few larvae that enter this restricted area and for evaluating the density and type of food organisms in the tank. A weaker, magnifying glass provides a greater depth of focus that takes in more area and can provide a better assessment of the condition of more larvae, their growth, feeding activity, gut contents, and general condition.

Dottyback grow-out substrate

Grow out of many species, such as clownfish and gobies, and probably even dottybacks can be done in a bare tank. The fish school together, tend not to develop defensive territories, and can be easily harvested. There is stress on the fish, however, when substrate shelter is not available to fish that are genetically programed to life in a dense reef environment. With the orchid dottybacks, I always provided ample benthic substrate beginning just before metamorphosis into the juvenile form. Territorial defense does occur, but if enough substrate is provided, very little of the aggression results in damage to individual fish.

This presents a problem, however, especially with species such as the orchid dottyback that enter very tiny crevices and holes in rocks and are very difficult to extract from these hiding places. Also a jumble of substrate on a tank bottom present a time consuming chore when the fish must be removed from the tank, since each piece must be removed and

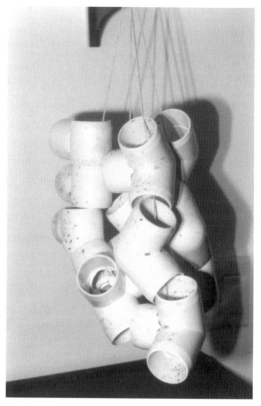

Like giant beads, PVC fittings strung on a string are easy to remove from the grow-out tank.

carefully examined before the fish can be harvested from the tank. There is a simple method of providing ample bottom substrate that can be quickly removed from the tank with without also removing the fish, even if the fish tenaciously occupy tiny holes and crevices. I simply cut many small sections of PVC pipe or use small fittings, one half to two inches in diameter, and string these on an ample length of nylon string. It is important not to put pieces next to each other that can tightly nest within each other, such as a short length of pipe and fitting for that same pipe diameter, since this will unduly increase the length and complexity of the internal area of this artificial substrate.

When it is necessary to remove fish, the "string of substrate" is slowly removed from the tank, the fish leave the relatively open pipe structure as it leaves the water, thus the entire substrate structure can be removed from the tank in one piece, leaving the fish behind in the now bare bottomed tank. After whatever fish required are caught and removed from the bare bottomed tank, the beaded pipe sections can be quickly replaced and the remaining fish quickly establish new territories in the reformed bottom substrate.

Spawning environment for the orchid dottyback

Knowing what type of micro habitat is required for a certain species of fish to comfortably spawn is quite important. It may be a hole of a particular depth or diameter, a flat surface, a type of algae or seagrass, a certain depth of water, the presence of a particular invertebrate, or any of a number of other conditions. Sometimes the right conditions are absolutely necessary for the spawn to occur, and other times it only helps the spawn to be more successful. In the case of the orchid dottybacks, a hole that the male can use for his spawning den, his bachelor pad, is important for sustained spawning. I was fortunate at first since the live rock that I placed in the tank had a natural hole of exactly the right dimensions. It had been formed by boring clams (they gave long lectures on how to dig holes) and has a small opening, about three quarters of an inch in diameter with a chamber about four inches long and about an inch in diameter. The male has used this chamber as a spawning den for over a year now. Such beautiful natural spawning dens are rare, however, so I have made similar dens from PVC pipe that work very well.

A short section, 4 to 5 inches, of thin walled, one inch diameter PVC pipe is capped on each end with a standard PVC pipe cap. The caps need not be glued, although it doesn't really matter. One of the caps has a half inch hole drilled in the center of the flat end. I usually enlarge this hole with a small grinder to almost three quarters of an inch in diameter. This provides a smaller entry way into the spawning chamber. I also drill a number of small holes, one eighth inch diameter, in the body of the pipe to allow for a better exchange of water in the chamber. The male entices the female into this chamber, spawning occurs, and then the male maintains the egg ball in the chamber until they hatch four days later. Spawning can occur in many other situations, such as between rocks, in sand areas under rocks, and other protected sites, but the pipe den allows for placement of the den in a spot that allows internal inspection with a flashlight

A male orchid dottyback leaves his made to order, PVC spawning den.

so that the presence and development of spawn can be monitored.

Imminent Reminder. The anti-overfill, resume filter operation, and brine shrimp settling reminder device

There is a period of time, usually in your early twenties, when you never forget anything important (although, in their 20's most people don't know too many important things—not you, of course, only other people in their 20's). This was so long ago for me, however, that I can't remember this time very clearly. Any other time of life, especially after 40, one can easily forget almost anything, even to zip up one's trousers, or lock the door, or where you last placed your glasses or keys. But nothing creates the great lamentations, and in some cases, spousal abuse, like forgetting that the hose is in the sump tank and water is slowly flowing into the system. Equally disastrous is to turn off the filter and water movement on a tank to look for the presence of larvae, forget to turn the filters on again, and later discover that your prize fish have "departed this mortal coil". Of less consequence, but nevertheless unsettling, is to forget until the next day that you left a hatch of brine shrimp to settle and separate before siphoning. Not that such things have ever happened to me. There is a way to provide a reminder of these events in progress so you won't forget and have to wade across the carpet.

This is the "Ray Lewis idiot proof remember method". Ray worked with me long ago and once in a while he, as did we all, might move on to other things and forget he was slowing filling a tank. This sometimes created vast overflows in the larval room that were only discovered when the downstairs ceiling above the grow-out tanks would begin to drip. To prevent this lapse of memory, Ray would put something

The latest fashion in "forget me not" aquarist apparel.

large and unwieldy, like a coffee cup or a hubcap, on a rope hung around his neck, and its presence would almost always remind him of the task in progress. I prefer something more subtle when my attention absolutely must be returned in 15 to 30 minutes to a task in progress. A film canister hanging on a string over my ear, or a piece of tape on my nose almost always reminds me to frequently check the progress of a fill, the settling of a hatch of brine shrimp, or even the slow siphoning of a larval tank.

Weigh outs

It can be difficult to weigh out small quantities of chemicals for treatments and trace elements if you don't have access to scientific laboratory equipment. For example, treating a 10 gallon tank with 50 milligrams per gallon of streptomycin sulphate requires the addition of 500 mg, a half a gram of this light, fluffy powder, to the rearing tank. Without a laboratory balance, this is not an easy task. It can be done reasonably accurately, however, with one of those little postal scales, the kind you hold in your hand and clip the envelope to a weighted arm with a ounce scale on one side of the indicator and a gram scale on the other side. The scale runs from 0 to 4 ounces and 0 to 100 grams with greatest accuracy in the first three quarter ounce (20 gram) range.

With tape, I attach a loop of string to a 35 mm film canister and hang this on the clip instead of an envelope. I then hang the scale from a shelf or other handy support and note the position of the indicator, right on 5 grams in my case. I then carefully add enough of the powder to bring the indicator to 6 grams, weighing out approximately 1 gram. For greater accuracy, 5 grams can be weighed out, and the greater the dilution, 500 or 1000 ml instead of 100 ml, for example, also increases accuracy. In this case, however, the one gram weigh out is accurate enough. The one gram of streptomycin is then dissolved in 100 ml of water. If 5 grams are weighed out, then those 5 grams are dissolved in 500 ml of water. Now we have a solution with about 1000 mg (1 gram) of streptomycin dissolved in each 100 ml of water or about 10 mg per ml. Adding 50 ml of this solution to a 10 gallon tank will deliver about 500 mg, about 50 mg of streptomycin per gallon.

There are other ways to weigh out very small quantities. For example, a simple balance can be made from dowels and a small nail, balancing two film canisters on string loops from

A simple postal scale, calabrated in grams, can be used for an approximate measure of small volumes.

each end of a length of dowel, and equaling the balance with small bits of clay stuck to either end of the dowel. A penny weighs 2.5 grams, a nickel weighs 5.0 grams, a dime weighs 2.3 grams and a quarter weighs 5.6 grams. Counterbalancing one or a combination of these coins will allow a relatively accurate measure of a few grams of dry chemicals.

Literature

Cited in Text

Brons, R. 1996. **Reproduction and Captive Breeding of two Red Sea Dottybacks**, *Pseudochromis fridmani* and *P. flavivertex*. FAMA. Vol. 19., No. 6: pp 48-54,58-62.

Brosseau, R. 1991. **Yet Another Clownfish Breeder.** Freshwater and Marine Aquarium Magazine. Vol. 14., No. 5, p 112-120.

Hoff, F. H. and T. W. Snell 1987. **Plankton Culture Manual.** Florida Aqua Farms, Inc., Dade City, FL, USA. 155 pp.

Hoff, F. H. 1996. **Conditioning, Spawning and Rearing of Fish with Emphasis on Marine Clownfish.** Aquaculture Consultants, Inc. Dade City, FL. USA. 212 pp.

Moe, M.A. Jr. 1989, (revised, 1992). **The Marine Aquarium Reference: Systems and Invertebrates.** Green Turtle Publications. Plantation, FL, USA. 512 pp.

Moe, M. A. Jr. 1992. **The Marine Aquarium Handbook: Beginner to Breeder.** Green Turtle Publications. Plantation, FL, USA. 320 pp.

Moe, M. A. Jr. 1997. **Spawning and Rearing the large Angelfish, Pomacanthus sp. Part 1.** Aquarium Frontiers, May/June 1997. pp 14-24. (Part 2 is in the first issue of the on-line publication of Aquarium Frontiers)

Wilkerson, J. D. 1992. *Amphiprion clarkii:* **Journey from Egg to Juvenile, Part 1**. Freshwater and Marine Aquarium Magazine, Vol. 15. No. 10, pp 17 -24. **Part 2**, FAMA , Vol. 15. No. 12, pp 154-162.

Young, F. A. 1991. **Rearing the Red Sea Anemonefish:** *Amphiprion bicinctus*. Freshwater and Marine Aquarium Magazine. Vol. 14., No. 4. p 136-142.

Suggested Readings
There are a great many books that are of interest to marine aquarists, with more being published every year. Books are knowledge, and they represent a great resource. An extensive book list will be part of the more conventional breeding book, but a short list of books is included here that will be of value to those interested in propagation of marine fish.

Adey, W.H. and K. Loveland. 1991. **Dynamic Aquaria**. Academic Press. San Diego, CA. USA. 643 p.

Allen, Gerald R. 1980. **Butterfly and Angelfishes of the World. Vol. 2: Atlantic Ocean, Caribbean Sea, Red Sea, Indo-Pacific.** Wiley-lnterscience, New York, N.Y. 352 pp.

Allen, Gerald R. 1980. **Anemonefishes of the World: Species, Care, and Breeding.** Aquarium Systems, Mentor, OH.104 pp.

Allen, Gerald R. 1975. **The Anemonefishes: Their Classification and Biology. (2nd Edition)** T.F.H. Publications, Inc., Neptune, N.J. 352 pp.

Austin, B. and D. A. Austin. 1987. **Bacterial Fish Pathogens: Disease in Farmed and Wild Fish.** Ellis Horwood Limited. West Sussex, England. 364 pp.

Bardach, J. E., Ryther, J. H. and W. O. McLarney. 1972. **Aquaculture: The Farming and Husbandry of Freshwater and Marine Organisms**. John Wiley & Sons, New York, NY. USA. 868 pp.

Bellomy, Mildred D. 1969. **Encyclopedia of Sea Horses.** T.F.H. Publications, Inc. Neptune, N.J

Breder, Charles M. Jr. and Donn E. Rosen 1966. **Modes of Reproduction in Fishes.** T.F.H. Publications, Inc. Neptune, N.J.

Colin, Patrick 1975. **The Neon Gobies.** T.F.H. Publications, Inc. Neptune, N.J. 304 pp.

Creswell, L.R. 1993. **Aquaculture Desk Reference**. AVI, Von Nostrand Reinhold. New York, NY. 206 pp.

Delbeek, J. C. and J. Sprung. 1994. **The Reef Aquarium.** Ricordea Publishing, Coconut Grove, Fla. USA. 544 pp

Dewey, D. (Editor) 1986. **For What It's Worth, Vol. 1.** *FAMA Anthology Lib. Ser.* R/C Modeler Corp. Sierra Madre, CA, USA 271 pp.

Escobal, P.R. 1996. **Aquatic Systems Engineering: Devices and How They Function.** Dimension Engineering Press, Oxnard, CA. 206 pp.

Fautin, D. G. and G. R. Allen. **Field Guide to Anemonefishes and their Host Anemones**. 1992. Western Australian Museum, Perth, WA. 160 pp.

Gratzek, J.B. (Editor, with J. R. Matthews) 1992. **Aquariology: The Science of Fish Health Management.** Tetra Press. Morris Plains, NJ. USA. 330 pp.

Herwig, N. 1979. **Handbook of Drugs and Chemicals used in the Treatment of of Fish Diseases**. Charles C. Thomas. Springfield, IL. 272 pp.

Hoff, F. H. and T. W. Snell 1987. **Plankton Culture Manual.** Florida Aqua Farms, Inc., Dade City, FL, USA. 155 pp.

Hoff, F. H. 1996. **Conditioning, Spawning and Rearing of Fish with Emphasis on Marine Clownfish.** Aquaculture Consultants, Inc. Dade City, FL. USA. 212 pp.

Iversen, E. S. and K.K. Hale. 1992. **Aquaculture Sourcebook: A guide to North American Species.** Von Nostrand Reinhold. New York, NY. USA. 308 pp.

Kingsford, Edward 1975. **Treatment of Exotic Marine Fish Diseases.** Palmetto Publishing Co., St.Petersburg, Fla. 92 pp. (out of print)

Lasker, R. (Editor) 1981. **Marine Fish Larvae.** Washington Sea Grant Program, University of Washington, WA. 131 pp.

Moe, M. A. Jr. 1991. **Lobsters: Florida, Bahamas, the Caribbean.** Green Turtle Publications. Plantation, FL, USA. 510 pp.

Moe, M.A. Jr. 1989, (revised, 1992). **The Marine Aquarium Reference: Systems and Invertebrates.** Green Turtle Publications. Plantation, FL, USA. 512 pp.

Moe, M. A. Jr. 1992. **The Marine Aquarium Handbook: Beginner to Breeder.** Green Turtle Publications. Plantation, FL, USA. 320 pp.

Needham, James G., F.E. Lutz, P.S. Welch and P.S. Galtsoff, Ed. 1937. **Culture Methods for Invertebrate Animals.** Comstock Publishing Company. Dover Edition 1959. Dover Publications, New York, N.Y. 590 pp.

Randall, J. E. 1965. **Food Habits of Reef Fishes of the West Indies.** *In* Studies in Tropical Oceanography, Vol. 5. pp 665-840.

Reichenbach-Klinke, HJ.-H. (1972) **Fish Pathology.** English translation, Christa Ahrens. TFH Publications. Neptune City, N.J. 512 pp.

Smith, D.L. and K. B. Johnson. 1996. **A Guide to Marine Coastal Plankton and Marine Invertebrate Larvae.** Second Edition. Kendall/Hunt Publishing Co. Debuque, IA. USA. 221 pp

Spotte, S. 1970. **Fish and Invertebrate Culture: Water Management in Closed Systems.** John Wiley & Sons. NY, USA. 145 pp.

Spotte, S. 1979. **Seawater Aquariums, The Captive Environment.** John Wiley & Sons. NY, USA. 413 pp.

Spotte, S. 1992. **Captive Seawater Fishes: Science and Technology.** John Wiley & Sons, Inc., New York, USA. 942 pp.

Sprung, J. 1995. **1. Reef Notes: Revisted and Revised.** Ricordea Publishing, Coconut Grove, FL. 184 pp.

Sprung, J. 1996. **2. Reef Notes: Revisted and Revised.** Ricordea Publishing, Coconut Grove, FL. 168 pp.

Sprung, J. 1996. **3. Reef Notes: Revisted and Revised.** Ricordea Publishing, Coconut Grove, FL. 168 pp.

Stoskopf, M.K. 1993. **Fish Medicine.** W.B. Saunders, Co. Philadelphia, POA. USA. 882 pp.

Thresher, Ronald E. 1980. **Reef Fish: Behavior and Ecology on the Reef and in the Aquarium.** Palmetto Publishing Company, St. Petersburg, Fla. 171 pp. (out of print)

Thresher, R. E. 1984. **Reproduction in Reef Fishes.** TFH Publications. Neptune City, N.J. 399 pp.

Tullock, J. H. 1994. **Successful Saltwater Aquariums.** Energy Savers Unlimited, Inc. Harbor City, Calif. USA. 164 pp

Wilkerson, J.D. 1997. **Clownfish: A Guide to their Captive Care, Breeding, and Natural History**, Microcosm LTD., Shelburne, VT. USA. 216 pp. (in press)

Periodicals
Aquarium Fish Magazine
Fancy Publications, Inc. 3 Burroughs, Irvine, CA. 92718

Aquarium Frontiers (on-line, internet publication) Aquarium Frontiers, P.O. Box 420593, Palm Coast, FL 32142

Freshwater and Marine Aquarium (FAMA) R/C Modeler Corp. P.O. Box 487, Sierra Madre, CA. 91024

Journal of Aquariculture and Aquatic Sciences
The Written Word. 7601 E. Forest Lakes Dr. NW, Parkville, MO. 64152

Journal of MaquaCulture
The Breeder's Registry, P.O. Box 255373, Sacramento, CA

Marine Fish Monthly
Publishing Concepts Corp. Main Street, Luttrell, TN. 37779

Sea Scope (a quarterly publication free to hobbyists)
Aquarium Systems, Inc. 8141 Tyler Blvd, Mentor OH 44060

Today's Aquarist
Todays Aquarist, 417 Bridgeport Ave., Devon CT 06460

Tropical Fish Hobbyist
T.F.H. Publications, Inc. One TFH Plaza, Neptune City, NJ. 07753

Marine Aquarium Societies, Hobbyist Organizations

Check your local aquarium shop for the names and addresses of local aquarium societies and clubs. All marine clubs and societies actively support captive propagation of marine organisms.

Marine Aquarium Society of North America
MASNA, P.O. Box 508 Penns Park, PA 18943 USA

The Breeder's Registry
P.O. Box 255373, Sacramento, CA 95865-5373

The marine aquarium societies of North America have worked together since 1989 to sponser a **Marine Aquarium Conference of North America (MACNA)** each year. Aquarium societies of the western US sponsor the **Western Marine Conference**, also an annual conference. These conferences are announced in aquarium hobby magazines and society newsletters.

Symbols, Measures, and Conversions

Abbreviations

Selected chemical symbols

Aluminum	Al	Hydrogen	H	Rubidium	Rb
Arsenic	As	Iodine	I	Potassium	K
Barium	Ba	Iron	Fe	Silicon	Si
Boron	B	Lead	Pb	Silver	Ag
Bromine	Br	Magnesium	Mg	Sodium	Na
Calcium	Ca	Manganese	Mn	Strontium	Sr
Carbon	C	Molybdenum	Mo	Sulphur	S
Chlorine	Cl	Mercury	Hg	Tin	Sn
Cobalt	Co	Nitrogen	N	Vanadium	V
Copper	Cu	Oxygen	O	Zinc	Zn
Fluorine	F	Phosphorus	P		

Selected chemical compounds

Ammonia, NH_3

Ammonium, NH_4^+

Bicarbonate, HCO_3^-

Calcium carbonate, $CaCO_3$
(chalk, calcite, aragonite)

Calcium chloride, $CaCl_{2)}$

Calcium hydroxide, $Ca(OH)_2$
(*Kalkwasser*, limewater)

Carbon dioxide, CO_2

Carbonate, CO_3^{2-}

Carbonic acid, H_2CO_3

Hydrogen sulfide, H_2S

Magnesium carbonate, $MgCO_3$

Nitrate, NO_3^-

Nitrite, NO_2^-

Sodium bicarbonate, $NaHCO_3$
(baking soda, bicarbonate of soda)

Sodium carbonate, dry, Na_2CO_3
(soda ash)

Sodium carbonate, crystalline, $NaHCO_3$ (washing soda, sal soda)

Sodium chloride, NaCl
(table salt, rock salt)

Sodium thiosulfate, $Na_2S_2O_3,5H_2O$
(hypo, dechlorinator)

Light
1 foot-candle = 1 lumen
1 candlepower = 12.56 foot-candles
1 Lux = 0.0929 foot-candles (or lumens)
1 lumen = 10.76 Lux
1 nanometer (nm) = 10 Angstroms (Å)

Temperature
Fahrenheit scale (°F): water freezes 32 °F, water boils 212 °F.
Centigrade (Celsius) scale (°C): water freezes 0 °C, water boils 100 °C.
Kelvin (Absolute) scale (°K): water freezes 273 °K, water boils 373 °K.
To convert °F to °C: (°F - 32) divided by 1.8 = °C
To convert °C to °F: (°C x 1.8) + 32 = °F

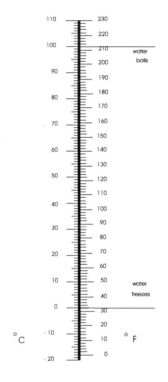

U K (British Imperial measure) conversions
(Courtesy of John Pointon)

US gallons   times 0.833 equals UK gallons
UK gallons   times 1.201 equals US gallons
UK pints   times 0.568 equals liters (Litres)
UK gallons   times 4.546 equals liters (Litres)
US gallons   times 3.785 equals liters (Litres)
liters (Litres) times 61.024 equals cu. inches
liters (Litres) times 0.035 equals cu. feet
liters (Litres) times 2.113 equals US pints
liters (Litres) times 0.264 equals US gallons
liters (Litres) times 1.756 equals UK pints
liters (Litres) times 0.220 equals UK gallons
one cu. foot seawater equals 6.228 UK gallons

UK gallons in a rectangular or square tank:
Length X Width X Height in inches and
divide by 277.42

UK gallons in a cylindrical tank:
diameter squared X 0.8 X height in inches
and divide by 277.42

One UK gallon seawater equals 10.2 lbs,
4.63 k, 277.42 cu. inches

Liquid measure

1 cubic centimeter (cc) = 1 ml, approximately 20 drops
1 milliliter (ml) = 1 cc, 1/1000 l
1 liter (l) = 1000 ml, 1.06 qt, 2.1 pt
20 large drops or 25 small drops = approximately 1 ml
1 teaspoon (tsp) = 5 ml, 1/6 fl oz
1 tablespoon (tbsp) = 3 tsp, 1/2 fl oz, 15 ml
1 fluid ounce (fl oz) = 2 tbsp, 6 tsp, 29.6 ml
1 cup = 8 fl oz, 236.8 ml
1 quart (qt) = 32 fl oz, 2 pt, 946.3 ml, 0.95 l
1 gallon (gal) 128 fl oz, 8 pt, 4 qt, 3.8 l, 231 in^3
1 part per million (ppm) = 1 ml or mg per l (ml/l), 3.78 mg/gal

Length

1 micron (μ) = 1/1000 mm
1 millimeter (mm) = 1/10 cm, 1000 microns, 0.039 in
1 centimeter (cm) = 10 mm, 0.39 in
1 meter (m) = 1000 mm, 100 cm, 39.37 in, 3.28 ft
1 inch (in) = 25.4 mm, 2.54 cm
1 foot (ft) = 12 in, 30.48 cm, 0.3 m
1 yard (yd) = 3 ft, 91.44 cm, 0.91 m

Weight
1 milligram (mg) = 1/1000 g
1 gram (g) = 1000 mg, 15.4 gr, 0.035 oz
1 kilogram (kg) = 1000 g, 35 oz, 2.2 lbs, one l pure water
1 grain (gr) = 0.65 g
1 ounce (oz) = 28.35 g
1 pound (lb) = 16 oz, 454 g, 0.45 k

Surface area (square measure, length X width)
1 square centimeter (cm^2) = 0.155 in^2
1 square meter (m^2) = 10,000 cm^2, 10.764 ft^2, 1555 in^2
1 square inch (in^2) = 0.007 ft^2, 6.45 cm^2
1 square foot (ft^2) = 144 in^2, 929.03 cm^2
1 square yard (yd^2) = 1296 in^2

Volume (cubic measure, length X width X height)
1 cubic centimeter (cm^3) = 0.061 in^3
1 cubic meter (m^3) = 11.77 ft^3, 1.31 yd^3
1 cubic inch (in^3) = 0.00058 ft^3, 16.387 cm^3
1 cubic foot (ft^3) = 1728 in^3, 0.765 m^3
1 gallon = 231 in^3

Formulas and data
1 ft^3 of seawater = 64 lbs, 29.02 k, 7.5 gal, 28.4 l, 1728 in^3, 3785.4 cc

1 gallon of seawater = 8.5 lbs, 3.86 k, 231 in^3

To find the number of US gallons in a rectangular or square tank
Multiply length X width X height in inches and divide by 231.

To find the number of US gallons in a cylindrical tank
Multiply the diameter squared X 0.8 X the height in inches and divide by 231.

To find the number of US gallons in a hexagon, octagon, or other multi-sided tank with sides of equal width, measure the total perimeter and multiply by the width of a single side. Then divide by 2, multiply by the height in inches, and divide by 231 to get the number of gallons.

To find the number of US gallons in a spherical tank, measure the radius (distance from the center to the edge of the sphere) in inches and cube this measurement (times itself by 3). Multiply this figure by 3.1416 (pi) and multiply the result by 1.33. Divide by 231 to get the volume of a sphere and again by 2 to get the volume of half a sphere.

Full salinity seawater contains 35 to 37 parts per thousand (ppt, ‰) salt. This is 35 to 37 grams per kilogram or liter, 4.7 to 5 oz per gal, and 2.9 to 3.1 lbs per 10 gal. *Approximately* 2.7 to 3 lbs of artificial sea salts make up 10 gal of full salinity seawater.

True specific gravity (sg) of full strength seawater (35 ‰) is 1.0260. A standard hydrometer calibrated at 59 °F (15 °C) reads 1.0234 sg at 77 °F (25 °C). Seawater at a salinity of 30 ‰ has a true specific gravity of 1.0222. At 30 ‰, a standard hydrometer reads 1.096 sg at 77 °F.

Index

About the Author

Martin A. Moe Jr. has been a marine biologist since 1960. He holds a masters degree from the University of South Florida and has worked as a fishery biologist, marine biologist, ichthyologist, and commercial marine fish breeder for over 35 years. His scientific and popular articles and books date back to 1962 when he began his career as a marine biologist for the State of Florida. He entered the private sector in 1969 and developed the basic technology for breeding Florida pompano in 1970. He accomplished the first commercial culture of marine tropical fish (clownfish and neon gobies) in a garage in 1972, and over the years has reared over 30 species of marine tropical fish, including spawning, rearing, and even hybridizing French and grey Atlantic angelfish. His latest rearing project was the propagation of the Red Sea orchid dottyback in a small fish room at home. Moe is the author of a definitive book on tropical Atlantic lobsters, *Lobsters : Florida • Bahamas • the Caribbean*, as well as his popular and best selling marine aquarium books, *The Marine Aquarium Handbook : Beginner to Breeder* and *The Marine Aquarium Reference: Systems and Invertebrates*. He founded Aqualife Research Corporation in 1972 and Green Turtle Publications in 1982. He and his wife Barbara now write and publish books on marine life and aquarium topics, and work with experimental keeping and rearing of aquatic organisms.

Books by Martin Moe

The Marine Aquarium Handbook :
Beginner to Breeder

A practical handbook on the theory and methods of keeping and breeding marine tropical fish. Everything you need to know to set up and maintain a successful saltwater aquarium. Set up and maintenance, trouble shooting, filtration, quarantine and disease, foods and feeding, and even breeding are discussed in detail in this best selling handbook. New edition revised and expanded in 1992.

320 pages   ISBN 0-939960-07-9 $16.95

The Marine Aquarium Reference :
Systems and Invertebrates

A major reference for the modern aquarist. This book contains 512 pages of text, tables, figures, and drawings that clearly and simply explain the techniques and technology of modern marine aquarium systems, including reef systems. *The Reference* clearly explains and integrates the new marine aquarium technology, trickle filters, high intensity lighting, gas reactors, denitrifying filters, protein foam skimmers, and many other advances with the traditional, established techniques of keeping marine aquariums. It also introduces the aquarist to the latest classification of invertebrates and other living organisms. This book is a companion volume to *The Marine Aquarium Handbook* .

512 pages   ISBN 0-939960-05-2 $21.95

Lobsters : Florida •Bahamas •the Caribbean

This is a comprehensive reference to the natural history, evolution, morphology, taxonomy, care and culture, and the recreational and commercial fisheries of the Caribbean spiny lobster, *Panulirus argus*. It includes a detailed description of larval rearing attempts on the the spiny lobster in the Florida Keys and a synopsis of the world wide literature on rearing and farming of spiny lobsters.

    512 pages   ISBN 0-939960-06-0 $22.95

Breeding the Orchid Dottyback, *Pseudochromis fridmani*: An Aquarist's Journal

In this book, Martin Moe brings you inside his home fish room, his daily routine, and his every thought and plan throughout a successful breeding project with the Red Sea orchid dottyback. Spawning requirements and behavior, larval rearing and feeding, food organism culture, fish grow out and much more is described in great detail in this book. It is more than a dry technical manual, however, it is a daily journey through failure and success leading to development of a workable technique for rearing marine tropical fish.

    288 pages   ISBN 0-939960-09-5 $19.95

You can borrow these books from your local library. You can purchase them at your local book store, aquarium shop, and at many public aquariums. If you can not find them locally, send your order to the address below. Please include $2 for shipping. Florida residents please include sales tax.

Green Turtle Publications
P.O. Box 17925
Plantation, FL 33318